SEX, MAN, AND SOCIETY

BY ASHLEY MONTAGU

The Human Revolution

Man's Most Dangerous Myth: The Fallacy of Race

The Humanization of Man

Man in Process

Human Heredity

The Cultured Man

Man: His First Two Million Years

Coming Into Being Among the Australian Aborigines

Edward Tyson, M.D., F.R.S. (1650–1708): and the Rise of Human and Comparative Anatomy in England

Statement on Race

The Direction of Human Development

The Natural Superiority of Women

The Reproductive Development of the Female

On Being Human

The Biosocial Nature of Man

Darwin, Competition and Cooperation

On Being Intelligent

Immortality

Education and Human Relations

Anthropology and Human Nature

Introduction to Physical Anthropology

Handbook of Anthropometry

Prenatal Influences

Race, Science, and Humanity

Life Before Birth

The Science of Man

The American Way of Life

The Anatomy of Swearing

Man Observed

Up the Ivy

The Idea of Race

Man's Evolution (with C. L. Brace)

Anatomy and Physiology (2 vols., with E. Steen)

The Dolphin in History (with John Lilly)

The Prevalence of Nonsense (with Edward Darling)

Fundamentals of Human Genetics (with Max Levitan)

Editor

Studies and Essays in the History of Science and Learning

Toynbee and History

The Meaning of Love

Genetic Mechanisms in Human Disease

International Pictorial Treasury of Knowledge

Atlas of Human Anatomy

Culture and the Evolution of Man

The Concept of Race

Culture: Man's Adaptive Dimension

The Concept of the Primitive

Man and Aggression

The Human Dialogue (with Floyd Matson)

Sex, Man,
and Society

by Ashley Montagu

G. P. PUTNAM'S SONS
NEW YORK

Acknowledgment is gratefully made to the following publications and publishers
for their permission to reproduce articles appearing in this book: *American
Anthropologist, American Journal of Orthopsychiatry, Ciba Symposia, Journal of
the American Medical Association, McCall's, Oceania, Phi Delta Kappan, Psychiatry, Quarterly Review of Biology, Science, Sexology*, Arts and Science Press,
Encyclopaedia Britannica, Greenberg (*Sex Life of the American Woman and the
Kinsey Report*), New American Library (*About the Kinsey Report, An Analysis
of the Kinsey Reports*).

Library of Congress Catalog Card Number: 70–81653

PRINTED IN THE UNITED STATES OF AMERICA

To *Geoffrey Montagu*

Preface

In this book are brought together some articles which I have written over a period of some thirty years on various aspects of sex. Some have previously appeared in print; some have not. With the deliberate exception of those on the Kinsey Reports all have been revised and been brought up to date. The process of revision was an enlightening experience. Looking back from the standpoint of the present, I found, for example, that changes in attitudes toward such things as premarital sex, virginity, the double standard, sex education, birth control, sex determination, and so on had proceeded at a much more rapid pace than most of my colleagues and I had anticipated. Most of the changes, if not all of them, it seems to me have been in the right direction. Gratifying as it is to observe these changes, it is very evident that we have a long way yet to go. We are greatly in need of more teaching of human relations, of sex education of both adults and the young, of population control, family planning, birth control, and a great deal else.

We need to replace fear and superstition with knowledge and understanding, and it is toward those ends that I hope this book may make some small contribution. In another work, *Man Observed* (New York: G. P. Putnam's Sons, 1968), I have dealt with the population problem. The nearest I get to that problem in the present book is in the discussion of the pill and in dealing with sex education. The matters of birth control, family size and spacing, quality control by quantity control, are implied even when they are not stated. The book, however, is of much wider scope than is embraced by such subjects, as will be seen from the table of contents. I have cast a rather extensive net over the many-faceted aspects of sex, and if the reader finds what I have written half as interesting as I found the research which led to these various studies, I shall be more than gratified.

ASHLEY MONTAGU

Princeton, New Jersey

Contents

SEX, MAN, AND SOCIETY

1. *The Pill, the Sexual Revolution, and the Schools*

The Pill! The fact that it is referred to so majesterially represents something of the measure of importance that is generally attached to this genuinely revolutionary development. For it *is* a revolutionary development, probably to be ranked among the half dozen or so major innovations in man's two or more million years of history. In its effects I believe that the pill ranks in importance with the discovery of fire, the creation and employment of tools, the development of hunting, the invention of agriculture, the development of urbanism, scientific medicine, and the release and control of nuclear energy.

This is rather a large claim to make, but I do not think that it is in the least exaggerated. The best way to substantiate this statement is to set out the facts and the consequences that are likely to ensue from the changes they imply. Since the consequences of the pill are likely to be manifold and profoundly alterative of age-old beliefs, practices, and institutions, it will be helpful to deal with the most significant of these in a systematic manner.

1. Birth control and its role in the humanization of man. For the first time in the history of man the pill provides a dependable means of controlling conception. For the first time, the pill makes it possible to render every individual of reproductive age completely responsible for both his sexual and his reproductive behavior. It is necessary to be unequivocally clear concerning the distinction between sexual behavior and reproductive behavior. Sexual behavior may have no purpose other than pleasure, pure hedonism or impure hedonism, without the slightest intention of reproducing, or it may be indulged in for both pleasure and reproduction. Sexual behavior is indulged in much more rarely for the purposes of reproduction than for the purposes of pleasure. Hedonistic sex is to be regarded as purely sexual behavior. Sex that is indulged with a view to the generation of children constitutes reproductive behavior. In these senses the female tends to be the reproductive creature and the male more often the sexual creature.

No society can tolerate any form of anarchic behavior in its midst, and therefore sexual promiscuity, that is, irresponsible sexuality, especially has been prohibited in all human societies. In all societies every individual is made responsible for (1) his sexual behavior and (2) his reproductive behavior. In nonliterate societies this has been regulated in the following manner: Sex for the sheer pleasure of it has been allowed everyone, but reproductive behavior has been permitted only to those persons who are married to one another. Since, in almost all such societies, girls marry at or shortly after the attainment of the first menstruation (menarche), premarital sexual relations practically never result in children,[1] so there are no problems. In marriage the number of children, especially at the food-gathering, hunting level of economic development, is planned. For example, in order to control the size of their families the Bushmen of the Kalahari desert simply abstain from sexual intercourse as the most effective means of birth control. The same is true of many other nonliterate peoples. The love and respect these peoples have for their children and for each other, and the vital necessity of controlling the size

[1] For a discussion of the physiology of this see Ashley Montagu, *The Reproductive Development of the Female* (New York: Julian Press, 1957).

of their families, as well as their population numbers, is something that we who have gone so far in the opposite direction must learn if we are again to be able to love our children and each other—indeed, if we are to survive at all.

With the gift of the pill we now have the power placed comfortably in our hands of accomplishing all these ends, and more. Until we do, the debasement of humanity which has proceeded at such an alarming rate in the recent period will continue in its destructive effects at an accelerating pace, until the very edge of doom. With the pill, not to mention the improved versions which are already in process of development, we have it in our power to begin the rehumanization of man at the very foundations. The task of making human beings out of people literally becomes impossible when their numbers exceed the limits consonant with a successful issue to such an undertaking. That, then, is the first of the contributions made by the pill: It provides the basis for the humanization of man.

2. *The sexual emancipation of the sexes.* In civilized societies the fear of conception has produced anxieties about sex in the female which have had a variety of effects upon the sexual relationship. Among these has been the strong resistance which females have traditionally offered against the male's sexual advances. Because of this resistance the male has been forced into a predatory exploitative attitude toward the female. With the freedom to enjoy sex for its own sake which the pill affords, women's attitudes toward sex will change, and the attitudes of men toward women will undergo a complementary change. The double standard, which has had so damaging an effect upon both sexes and upon our society, will make way for a healthier view of sex and of the relations between the sexes.

It will become possible for the first time for the sexes genuinely to complement each other, and to live and love together on a basis of full equality. The shortsighted "viewers with alarm" will be relegated to their proper places when what they so wrongheadedly deplore, the alleged feminization of men and the alleged masculinization of women, are discovered to be advances in the right rather than in the wrong direction.

It is only in recent years that we have learned that what we have always taken for granted as biologically determined, namely, masculinity and feminity, are in fact genders which are virtually wholly culturally determined. We now know, beyond dispute, that whatever the biological sex of the child may be, its gender role, that is, its social role, is what it *learns*. One learns to be either male or female according to the manner in which one is socialized, or to put it more accurately, *gender-ized*.[2] Hence, when one sex assumes some of the behaviors traditionally associated with the other, no violence is done to any putative biological functions. Males have long stood in need of such feminine qualities as tenderness, sensitivity, compassion, gentleness, and the like. Women, for their part, will benefit from the adoption of traits hitherto considered purely masculine, such as courage, adventuresomeness, enterprise, intrepidity, and the like. Men need to be humanized; women to be energized. Men need to become more secure, compassionate, and less violent. Women, to achieve their full status as human beings, need men to go with them who have also acquired or are on the way to acquiring that status.[3]

3. *The social emancipation of women.* Possibly the greatest revolution resulting from the advent of the pill is the social emancipation of women that it will bring about. Menstruation, for example, for virtually all women has been to some extent socially handicapping. Because of it, in a male-dominated world, the female has everywhere been relegated to "the menstrual hut," discriminated against, and permanently demoted in the hierarchy of statuses. Furthermore, many women during the menstrual cycle have been the captives of their hormones, often

2 See John Money (ed.), *Sex Research: New Developments* (New York: Holt, Rinehart & Winston, 1965). Robert J. Stoller, *Sex & Gender* (New York: Science House, 1968).

3 For a discussion of these matters see Vance Packard, *The Sexual Wilderness* (New York: David McKay Co., 1968).

moody, affected by premenstrual tensions, and not infrequently "ill." All these things have in the past combined to make menstruation a "curse" for women physiologically and psychologically. The pill, by inhibiting the processes that lead to menstruation, while it is taken, suppresses that function and frees women for the first time from the discomforting and often disabling effects of menstruation and the possibility of unwanted pregnancy. With all these psychologically handicapping conditions which were formerly incident to her physiology removed, the last of the grounds for discrimination against women is removed, and women may at long last enter into that full social equality which, until the development of the pill, was so long denied them.

The pill in its present form, effective as it is, is but the precursor of more sophisticated forms of hormone regulators, as they may be called. Pills are already in process of development which are designed to produce long-term inhibition of ovulation, conception, and menstruation. A single pill will produce immunity for years, its inhibitory effects being cancelable at will by taking another pill that restores the normal physiological functions.

Foresight is the last of the gifts granted by the gods to man. All the more reason, therefore, to reflect upon and prepare for the developments which these revolutionary changes, in the very beginnings of which we are now living, will bring about. This is nowhere more important than its effects upon the young.

4. Premarital sex. The prohibition against sex in civilized societies, in which the age of marriage is delayed well into reproductive development, has a long and interesting history behind it. In the Western world the attitudes, customs, practices, and beliefs concerning the relations of the sexes to each other in all age grades and statuses have largely been transmitted through the teachings of the Judeo-Christian tradition. Since in such societies children born out of wedlock had no legal father, nor for that matter a legal mother, and since society was so structured as to offer no means of incorporating the child, and often the mother, into the society, and since sexual intercourse outside of wedlock was itself stigmatized as a sin, the negative sanctions against such immoral and illicit sex were severely enforced. Thus, premarital sex came to be held as morally, legally, and socially abhorrent. Virtually all the reasons created to justify the prohibitions against premarital sex were little more than rationalizations. These concealed the real reasons why premarital sex could not be tolerated in such societies, namely, the havoc such disallowed conduct caused to the flying buttresses of the social and religious organization of such societies. The ostracism and punishments that were often inflicted upon the offenders served as sufficient deterrents to prevent premarital intercourse from growing to unmanageable proportions. But with the advent of two world wars and the breakdown in moral, religious, and social values that followed upon them there was a notable increase in all forms of forbidden sex.

The Kinsey Reports, with which we shall deal later in the book, in part, constitute a monumental record of the status of sexual mores in the mid-twentieth century. Kinsey found that there was a great deal more covert sexual activity of every forbidden kind than was overtly admitted or even suspected. In the 1960's the pregnancy rate of girls of school age has risen spectacularly. These are facts which must be squarely faced.

It is not, for many reasons, desirable for girls of school age to bear children. In the first place, they are physiologically unprepared in most cases for such a function, with the result that a large proportion of children born to such immature mothers suffer from all sorts of deficiencies. This would be reason enough to discourage early pregnancy, but in fact it constitutes the last of the reasons why early pregnancy should be discouraged. The primary reason for such discouragement is that adolescent girls are themselves in process of development, of maturation as persons, and are in every way socially and psychologically unready for the responsibilities of motherhood. The optimum age for childbearing from every point of view, physiological, psychological, and social, is between twenty-three plus or minus two years and twenty-eight plus or minus two years. Childbearing before the age of twenty-three plus or minus two years should therefore be discouraged.[4]

With the pill, premarital sex without any of the anxieties usually associated with it or the birth of children becomes for the first time possible, and hence the principal barrier against it is removed. But with the removal of this barrier the responsibilities involved in this particular relationship are maximized beyond anything that has hitherto been anticipated or required. For once the barrier has been lowered, the danger of the debasement of this delicate, this tender, this most sensitive of all human relationships is greatly increased. Hence, no one should ever think of entering into such a relationship who is incapable of behaving responsibly in it. Responsibility to others is something one must learn. It is not something one is born with. It is here that the schools must assume *their* responsibility, for it is in the schools that the parents of future generations must be prepared in the meaning of sex and responsibility. What then is sexual responsibility, and how can it be taught in the schools?

5. *Sexual responsibility.* By "responsibility" I essentially mean involvement in the welfare of the other. It seems to me that involvement in the welfare of others should constitute the basis of all human relationships. If one cares about others, it is difficult, possessed of the requisite knowledge and responsibility, to behave in such a manner as to harm one's fellowman. It is necessary, however, to underscore the fact that involvement is not enough, because without the requisite knowledge and sensitivity, it is possible, with the best of intentions, to wreak havoc upon others. The evil that well-intentioned people have done adds up to a sizable quantity. It is not enough to be good; it is

4 See Montagu, *op. cit.*

necessary also to be knowledgeable and understanding. All these qualities can be and should be taught in the schools. They should, of course, also be taught in the home. But unless we can satisfactorily establish the criteria by which the good, the true, and the beautiful can be measured, we shall not get very far in the discussion of sexual responsibility. I mention the "true" and the "beautiful" because these are fundamentally the same as "knowledge" and "understanding." Let us further define our terms. Goodness or love is behavior calculated to confer survival benefits in a creatively enlarging manner upon the other. It is conduct which enables the other not only to live but to develop and live more fully realized than he would have had you not communicated to him your involvement in his welfare.

By "knowledge" is to be understood verifiable information, and by "understanding" is to be understood the ability to appreciate what that knowledge is capable of doing, not merely what knowledge *is* but what it is *for*.

Sexual responsibility, as every other kind of responsibility, implies moral involvement, the moral responsibility to be responsible to others for oneself and for them. This implies the goodness, the knowledge, and the understanding of what in the special case of sexual behavior are the indispensable qualifications before one may enter into any sexual relationship. Spelled out in practical terms, what this means is that our schools must become institutes for the teaching of human responsibility, with this as the primary purpose of education and with instruction in the three R's purely secondary to this main purpose. To understand the nature of human nature is not beyond the capacity of a child; comprehension of the vulnerabilities of human beings, sensitivity to the needs of others, thoughtfulness and consideration, the facts about sex, its philosophy, psychology, and ethics, can be taught at every school age. Courses in these subjects, can, of course, be graduated to meet the requirements of the young at every age.

What will be required will be skillfully organized teaching materials and well-trained congenially sophisticated teachers. Our teachers' colleges are at the present time, for the most part, wholly unequipped to prepare such teachers. Hence, a tremendous amount of work needs to be done, and most of it, it is to be feared, will be done by trial and error—which is better than not being done at all. However it be done, it were well that it were done as soon as possible, for the hour is late and human beings are much in need of that goodness, knowledge, and understanding for lack of which so many avoidable tragedies have blighted the lives of countless individuals and families. Never was there a period more favorable than the present in which to introduce into our schools the teaching of sexual responsibility. The sexual revolution should precipitate the educational revolution, which should in turn swiftly lead to the human revolution.

Let me explain. The teaching of sexual responsibility can be a fascinating experience for both teacher and pupil. It is not only an extremely interesting subject in itself, but since it gets down to the fundamentals of human relationships, it constitutes a uniquely sensitive introduction to the whole world of human relations. This is how, I believe, the course on sexual responsibility (or whatever other name it may be called by) should be taught, not as a course on sex but as a part of the course on human relations. Thus, one would begin with the exciting evolutionary history of the manner in which human beings got to be the way they are now, what it means to be human from the evolutionary point of view, the nature of human nature, the facts about the physiology and psychology of reproduction, birth, the needs of the newborn, and the means of its humanization.[5] By such a route we might for the first time genuinely

---

[5] In these connections see the following books by Ashley Montagu: *The Human Revolution* (New York: Bantam Books, 1967); *The Direction of Human Development* (New York: Harper, 1955); *The Humanization of Man* (New York: Grove Press, 1963).

realize the purposes of education: the making of fulfilled humane beings, the making of humane beings out of people.

It will take time. How long will depend on how widespread this kind of teaching becomes throughout the land. Toward the furtherance of that end it would be a great boon if we could drop the euphemistic phrase "the facts of life." The facts of life are strictly for the birds, the bees, and the bats, especially the bats that are addicted to belfries. What growing young human beings need is understanding of their own growth and development, how they came into being, and what their presence upon this earth in fact means for the great and continuing enterprise of human relations. And that is the point, I believe, that should be the main theme of education in sexual responsibility—what one owes to others and what one has a right to expect from others as humanely accomplished human beings. As I have already remarked, education in sexual responsibility becomes essentially education in human sensitivity, in knowledge, understanding, and loving-kindness.

Young unmarried individuals who are sufficiently responsible will be able, in the new dispensation, to enter into responsible sexual relationships in a perfectly healthy and morally acceptable and reciprocally beneficial manner, which will help the participants to become more fully developed human beings than they would otherwise have stood a chance of becoming. The dead hand of ugly traditional beliefs, which has been responsible for untold human tragedies, will be replaced by a new flowering of human love. This is a critical point.

6. *Love.* Love, for far too many males in the Western world, has been confused and identified with sex. Females for such men have amounted to little more than sexual objects. Such attitudes on the part of men have resulted in the debasement of the most important of all human relatednesses—the ability to love.

Love is by far the most important of all the needs which must be satisfied if the growing creature is to be humanized. It stands at the center of all the other needs, like the central sun in our solar system around which the other planets move in their orbits. It is the one and only need which must be adequately satisfied if we are to become healthy human beings. By health I mean the ability to love and the ability to work. Spelled out, love means the communication of one's deep involvement in the welfare of the other, the communication of one's profound interest in the realization of the other's potentialities for being the kind of human being you are being to him. It means the communication of the feeling that you will always be standing by, that you will never commit the supreme treason that human beings so frequently commit against their fellowman, of letting him down when he most stands in need of you, but that you will be standing by, giving him all the supports and sustenances and stimulations that he requires for becoming what it is in him to be. Knowing that to be human is to be in danger, to be terribly vulnerable to the damage that people are capable of inflicting upon one another, that you will be particularly careful, in caring for the other, not to commit such errors. If one can communicate these messages to the other, then I believe one can be said to love him. And this is the sort of thing that we should be teaching in our schools. As I have said, this should be the primary purpose of the schools. Within the matrix of such teaching a special course on sexual responsibility would hardly be necessary, except insofar as details were concerned.

As a corollary of this discussion on love, it should follow that those who are unable to love in this manner should refrain or else be discouraged from entering into human relationships involving the deepest sensibilities of others. The irresponsible should be rehabilitated as human beings before they are permitted to enter into such relationships.

7. *Marriage.* From the above discussion it should also follow that no one who is unprepared for marriage, as a person aware of all that is required of one in the marital relationship, should be permitted to marry. Certainly everyone should always re-

main free to choose whom he desires to marry, but fitness for marriage should be determined by the state until such time as human beings have attained the maturity and responsibility to make such decisions for themselves. At the present time most persons are certainly not able to do so; hence the enormous separation, divorce, and broken home rates.

Furthermore, the ability to pass a marriageability test is not to be regarded as *prima facie* evidence of the ability to relate oneself to children responsibly. Hence, tests of fitness for the parental role, giving evidence of ability to minister responsibly to the needs of children, would first have to be passed before anyone was permitted to bring a child into the world. Nor, of course, should anyone who is unfit for the task of responsible parenthood be permitted to adopt children.

Those who do pass the tests for responsible parenthood will understand the importance of spacing the births of their children. They will plan the spacing and the number of children they propose to have, and in this connection there are unlikely to be the slightest problems. However, these are matters which will require careful teaching long before the principals involved reach the stage of seriously contemplating parenthood. Hence, as part of the teaching of sexual responsibility, I would make the teaching of birth control and the spacing of births an integral part of the course taught at progressively sophisticated levels as the level of maturity of the student increases.

Since nothing can concern the individual or the state more than the quality of the citizenry, the state must assume the regulation of that quality. This is dangerous doctrine, for obviously in the hands of the wrong people great havoc could by this means be wrought. But I am not thinking in terms of the wrong people or of dictators. I am thinking of a democracy. Democracy is, however, a form of government which can work only as well as its citizens want it to. It demands a great deal of work on the part of its citizens. The citizens of a democracy must be taught to be worthy of it; otherwise they will get exactly the kind of government they deserve. Democracy is a privilege, and privileges entail obligations. Our job as teachers and parents should be to make democracy work by teaching the young what the obligations of a citizen worthy of a democratic government should know and do. The first thing I would teach our developing citizen is that the most important quality of a human being is the ability to relate himself to others in a warm, loving manner, as one who is capable of using his mind as the finely analytical instrument it is capable of becoming, joining knowledge, understanding, sensitivity, and responsibility to loving-kindness. Possibly by such means we would produce human beings who through their own understanding and self-discipline would render wholly unnecessary any state-administered tests of fitness. It is, of course, this that we should aim for through our socialization and educational processes.

2. Sex Education: Children and Adults

Parents and the community find themselves in the middle of a revolution which they did not foresee, and for which they are, for the most part, unprepared. Thinking about the unthinkable with ideas that for any applicability they may have for the new age in which we live might just as well belong to the Dark Ages, they not only are caught unprepared but are not a little bewildered. How then are parents and the community to adapt themselves to the new sexual revolution?

Those parents who are able to do so will have to take the initiative by making themselves, as a first step, personally responsible for the sex education of their children. As a second step, parents must see to it that sex education becomes part of the general education of their children, that an education in sex is provided in our schools from the earliest ages, and that education in sex be at least as thorough as education in any other subject. At the present time sex education in our schools is practically nonexistent. Some idea of the extent to which our society shies away from what would, in any reasonable society, be regarded as an indispensable part of the individual's education may be gathered from the following facts. In a study designed to discover what was being done about sex education in American schools, a nationwide survey was made in 1965 by the Health Guidance in Sex Education Committee of the American School Health Association. The appalling number of forty out of many thousands of schools that were circularized responded to the questionnaire. Of this small number, about 80 percent had some form of sex education, but quite clearly, in most cases, this was of the most inadequate kind. In California, that land of perpetual pubescence, only 26 percent of the schools had any courses in family living or sex education in their curricula.

In 1965 the School Health Education Study sponsored by the U.S. Public Health Service, the National Congress of Parents and Teachers, the American Medical Association, the U.S. Office of Education, and the National Education Association inquired into the subject of sex education in 1,101 elementary schools with a total enrollment of more than 500,000, and in 359 high schools with more than 300,000 students. This study revealed that resistance on the part of parents and the community to the discussion of sex, venereal disease, and related matters constituted the main cause of the general ignorance among children of these important aspects of health. Other factors were ineffectual instruction methods, inadequate time devoted to health instruction, inadequate preparation of teachers, and indifference on the part of some teachers, as well as students, parents, health officers, administrators, and other members of the community. It was found that more than 70 percent of high school seniors entertained some rather serious misconceptions concerning sex and health. It is just this sort of ignorance that can be corrected in our schools.

For more than a decade Sweden has, by law, instituted the teaching of the facts about sex in its public schools. Sweden affords us a pilot study which, without the cost of a single penny to ourselves, at least indicates what can be achieved by sex education in the schools of a sensible society. All is by no means perfect, but the healthiest kind of progress has been made. So much so that the young clamor for fuller and more detailed teaching of the facts about the science and art of sex. Even in Sweden there are still some teachers who feel somewhat embarrassed in talking to young people about sex. My own view is that courses in sex should be given by teachers who both by training and by personality are able to communicate a sensitive understanding of the nature of sex and its practice. Furthermore, as in Sweden, boys and girls should be taught in the same classroom, so that they do not develop that unfortunate awkwardness which so often occurs in the absence of such joint experience, but develop instead healthier, open-minded attitudes toward sex which will relieve them of the intimidating embarrassments that afflict so many people throughout their lives whenever the word "sex" is mentioned.

Why should not a boy and a girl be able to talk freely with each other about sex, just as they might about any other activity, as long as it is done with a proper respect for each other, without prurience, without presumption, and from the healthiest of motives: the desire to know, to understand, and to live life as happily as one ought? And one ought to live as if to live and love were one.

What does a mother do when her daughter says, "Sex is my business. It is not yours"? As a broad generalization I would suggest complete honesty and something along the line of: "Of course, sex is your business, but it is also your responsibility. Are you prepared to deal with it responsibly?" It is at that point that the discussion can be initiated regarding maturity, vulnerability, and all the problems which opportunistic, irresponsible, and immature attitudes toward sex can create. And the same, of course, holds true for boys.

In all education the objective should be to assist the growing person to realize his potentialities for involvement and mutual aid. In a competitive society in which the ideal and the real cultures are two very different things, it may be difficult to oppose the real culture with the principles of the ideal culture, but it is not a difficulty which is insuperable. The time to start is in infancy, but it cannot be too strongly emphasized that no one is more avid for, more ready to receive, the best that experience, knowledge, understanding, and wisdom have to offer him than the adolescent.

It is essential for parents, the schools, and the community to recognize that children at the threshold of adolescence, and especially adolescents, are a good deal "older" than they used to be in earlier generations. They are not only physically better grown but psychologically and socially more mature. They understand more and are responsive to a much wider range of experience than their compeers were only a generation or two ago. Hence, instead of being more difficult, communication ought to be much easier between the generations than was the case only a short time ago.

The generation gap is not unbridgeable. What it in fact means is the failure of the older to understand the younger generation. If adults will be willing to consider that possibility, instead of taking the authoritarian view that they know what is best without having for a moment contemplated the possibility that what may have been "best" for them a generation ago may not necessarily be so for their children a generation later, progress will be made.

Adults must recognize, as they must also come to understand, the great desire and need of all children, and most particularly adolescents, to have the firm assurance of the adult world in their welfare; not mere meaning well but active involvement, the sympathy, understanding, guidance, absence of captiousness, and love which they find only too often lacking in the world.

If the adult world were less obsessed by sex and more concerned with the quality of human relations, discussions such as this would scarcely be necessary. The mental fig leaves which until recently made all open discussion of sex impossible have to some extent fallen away, but they have not yet been accompanied by the dissolution of that awkwardness which afflicts so many adults when it comes to a free discussion of the subject.

It should be evident, then, that what is required is not so much sex education for children as sex education for adults. In a "child-centered" society the focus of attention is on the child. But since it is adults who create children, psychologically and socially as well as biologically, it should surely be obvious that until we can create adults who are capable of thinking and feeling healthily and soundly about human relations in general, and about sexual relations in particular, we are not likely to enjoy as great success with sex education in children as we would were we ourselves in a better state of health.

3. Sex and Parents

The ignorance, misinformation, and downright non-sense which characterizes what is almost euphemistically called sex education constitutes a dark arcanum of malfunctioning that has serious consequences for far too many human beings.

The load of guilt feelings that most people carry as a consequence of this ignorance, the unfortunate depressing effects which such guilt feelings exert upon their personalities, the inability of so many women to experience orgasm, the sexual awkwardness and lack of understanding and all that that implies on the part of so many males, the marital and family tragedies, the human, social and economic wastage, add up to a terrific cost, not one iota of which is necessary or anything but undesirable.

Sex is the most wonderful thing in the world; next to the love of a mother for her child, it is the most beautiful experience in relation to another person which any human being can enjoy. All the more reason then why every child, man, and woman should understand its meaning to the full.

Many parents take the view that sex education should not be initiated before adolescence, and some prefer it to be a good deal later. But whatever such parents may think, the fact is that their children's education in sex begins well within the first year of life and what they don't learn themselves or from their parents they will learn from other and usually not the best sources.

31

When parents, from shyness or sheer lack of know-how or for any other reason, discourage the child's healthy attempts to learn something about sex, by the time the child is ready for school he will already know that sex is one of those dark, mysterious realms of forbidden knowledge about which it is somehow "naughty" and "bad" to exhibit curiosity.

The child should be permitted to pass so ill prepared into the new world of the school. Questions about sex should be answered as frankly and as clearly as possible. A child's usually healthy curiosity as to his own genesis or any act or reference to any act of a sexual nature should equally be healthily answered and not made the occasion for informing him that he is naughty or bad. To a child it is a condemnation of himself as bad when he is told that any act of his is bad.

The child is the most "curious" creature in the world. He has to be. For him life is an exploration, and among his earliest explorations is the discovery of his own body. In the course of this exploration he discovers that certain areas of his body yield sensations which are pleasurable. He discovers his mouth, his lips, and his genitals in this way.

Every child plays with his genitals. It is completely and perfectly normal to do so. And the discovery that a child does so is no more occasion for anxiety or punishment than is the act of breathing.

The notion that masturbation is "bad" is a most unfortunate myth. Masturbation is a normal part of the psychosexual development of every individual, a preparation for that fuller sexual life which he will attain as an adult. It is completely untrue that masturbation is debilitating or that it leads to insanity or any other harmful effect.

What leads to harmful effects are the scolding and disapproval which are visited upon the child by his parents or others for indulgence in this perfectly normal experience. The damage is done by causing the child to develop feelings of guilt about this activity and thus associate confused and anxious ideas about the terrible things that may happen to him as a result of his "wickedness." In this way anxieties are created, fears and repressions which will but serve to increase his emotional difficulties as a child and in later life.

Children should receive no discouragement from becoming acquainted with their own bodies and those of other persons of the same and the opposite sex. Healthy curiosity should be encouraged, and pruriency of any sort discouraged. And in this nothing can be of greater help than the healthy attitudes of the parents themselves in all situations involving sex.

If the natural curiosity of the child is satisfied at each stage of his development, he will undoubtedly avoid the tumultuous, fearful, and handicapping anxiety which is so often associated with the subject, and he will develop a healthy attitude toward sex.

A child needs to have his basic needs satisfied, and these will be most adequately satisfied if he enjoys the wholehearted love of his parents. If he has that, he will feel secure, and he will not need to look abnormally to his own body for satisfactions. If he is intimidated as a "bad" child, his fears and anxieties, generated by the loss of love with which he believes he is threatened, will become disturbingly great. He may exhibit these in tantrums, bed-wetting, nightmares, and aggressiveness, and the effect upon his personality may be *permanent*.

Excessive masturbation is often the result of its disapproval by the parent. It is at once a desire to recover some of the love that has been lost, a protest, and the performance of an act which has been given a disproportionately heavy emotional weighting by its interdiction. Such behavior causes the child to worry more, to feel more guilty, and the more he worries the more he masturbates. Excessive masturbation is therefore often a symptom that the child is emotionally disturbed.

All this can be completely avoided by a reasonable and understanding attitude on the part of the parents in the first place. Masturbation is nothing to worry or to do anything about. Let it take its normal course, and all will be well—provided, of course, that in most other things relating to the child his needs are reasonably well satisfied. The child needs his parents' love beyond all other things. It is through the parents' love that the greater part of the child's struggle for emotional well-being is won. The child needs playmates, plenty of activity, and the encouragement of his interests. He needs his questions answered and his curiosity satisfied.

Ordinarily it is quite unnecessary to discuss the subject of masturbation with the child. There is not the least necessity to draw attention to it. If others have done so, and have worried him about it, he should be reassured and told that some people don't think it desirable, but that it is not really important. Most children do it, and there is nothing harmful in it. For this is the truth, the whole truth, and nothing but the truth.

Bringing up a child is the most important job any person can ever be called upon to perform. Most people don't seem to realize this; they enter upon the parentage as if it were something one needs to know no more about than breathing. As every one of them soon discovers, there is a great deal more to parentage than having babies. It is really a full-time job.

If one is going to become a doctor, a lawyer, a baker, or a candlestick maker, he certainly has to learn the necessary skills in order to qualify. It may be said that parenthood is not a profession or a trade. In the ordinary sense perhaps not, but in a sense more profound than the ordinary, parenthood, not parentage, is older than the "oldest profession" in the world and certainly the most ancient trade.

The profession of parenthood is the process of earning a living for one's children, *not* alone earning a living in the ordinary sense of supplying them with food, shelter, and clothing but earning a life by molding, helping to form and guide, the child's personality. In that sense the profession of parenthood is also a trade, a trade between parents and experience in affecting the lives of their children.

Surely one should have more than an intuitive equipment in the art and science of making a human being. Depending upon the kind of sex education he receives during the first few years of his life, a human being can be either made or marred.

It should be part of the community's function, therefore, to see to it that every potential parent receives adequate instruction in the purposes and practices of child-rearing. This, of course, will embrace a good deal more than sex education, but no part of such instruction will be more important than that which is devoted to sex education.

In the schools it will not be enough to delegate a teacher to read up on the subject and then give an innocuous talk on the sex life, well wrapped in oblique phrases relating to the birds, the bees, and the beetles. Instruction in sex education must be given by teachers who have been specially trained to teach the subject.

This puts a further obligation upon our teacher-training colleges to see to it that the subject of sex education receives adequate emphasis in the training of *all* potential teachers, so that in the schools *every* teacher is fully equipped to handle the subject.

Lectures to teachers and to parents by experts on sex education and recent developments in it are much to be encouraged, but must not remain the sole pabulum upon which these educators rely for nourishment. It is the health of their charges which is at stake, and nothing short of the best and the most efficient will do.

In addition, it is necessary to understand that education is not simply a matter of school and home but that a very considerable part of it occurs in the world outside these two institutions. The child wants to be like other children and usually models his behavior after the pattern set by his peers. The confusions which the home has generated in him with regard to all matters relating to sex will be resolved, usually in the most undesirable of ways, by what he learns from other children. Smut and dirty stories, obscene language and gestures, all experienced under the aura of the forbidden yet desirable, unhealthily focus the child's attention upon the tabooed lustful aspects of sex.

Under such conditions sex soon becomes established in the child's mind as something immoral, indecent, dirty, but very desirable and gratifying. As he grows older, the movies, "best sellers" of the most meretricious kind, the lurid reporting of sex crimes by the press, and the marketing and sale of sex all conspire to titillate the child's growing preoccupation with the forbidden pleasures of sex.

One of the most unfortunate and tragic results of all this is that the growing individual comes to regard sex not only as something forbidden and lustful but as something to be thought of purely in terms of *self*-gratification. Sex becomes a matter of relieving one's own tensions by doing something *to* the sexual *object*.

The four-letter words which regularly describe sexual intercourse all clearly imply this attitude toward sex. Not only is self-indulgence the theme of such terms; there is also a strong element of bravado in the consciousness of having successfully broken taboos and made another "conquest." A man, under such conditions, often measures his own sexual quality by the number of conquests he has thus made.

When sex grows to be regarded as a chronic irritation which must be relieved through some object having the necessary requirements of sexual attractiveness, sex is then sick, pathological. And that, unfortunately, is what sex is in the United States today. It is largely for this reason, we may suspect, that one in every three marriages in the United States today ends in separation or divorce.

When sex becomes identified with self-gratification, the person is unable to "give" of himself to another. He remains a self-gratifier, not an "other" or "reciprocal" gratifier. His motives in sexual intercourse are entirely selfish, and this occurs in a relationship in which the chief purpose should be complete identification with another person, the gratification of both as a unity, not the gratification of oneself alone.

This latter is a confession of tragic failure, not as much because it is a failure to satisfy one's partner as because fundamentally it is also a failure to satisfy oneself. The fundamental human relationship is a cooperative one, and when there is a failure of cooperation there can be no satisfaction of a need which is essentially cooperative.

The truth of this is all too frequently seen in the quest for a variety of sex experience, whether it be in the number of different conquests or the variety of sexual techniques. These are invariably found to fail to satisfy the need for that "something" that is missing, that "something" which constitutes the ability to "share" fully and healthily in the experience of sex.

Women often complain of their husband's lack of sexual tenderness. But how can a man be tender when what he has been conditioned to in regard to sex is lust and lewdness? How can he be other than coarse and crude? All his life he has been exposed to sex as something "dirty," "obscene," "lewd," and "salacious." Tenderness is the one thing that he has *never* been exposed to in this connection. How, then, can we expect the malleable, impressionable, conditionable human being to behave other than in the manner to which he has been accustomed —unless we teach him otherwise, early enough?

More than half a century ago Bernard Shaw described marriage as "licensed prostitution." Never before have his words been as true as they are today. When the charms of the spouse have ceased to please, the marriage is virtually at an end. "Love" has become identified with "sexual attraction." Respect, sympathetic understanding, interdependency, identification, companionship, character, the elements of which true love in marriage is compounded, have been virtually completely displaced by the addiction to "sexual love."

Is it then any wonder that when the excitements of the first few months of marriage have begun to pall, so-called "love" quickly fades, and new sexual excitements are looked for elsewhere? Poor human beings, caught in a trap which was none of their own devising! Victims of an insane conspiracy of silence and confusion which serves to rob them of equilibrium and happiness. Such is the effect of our present mores with respect to sex education.

What a price to pay for prejudice and ignorance! What a pass has a people come to if every third marriage must end in disaster. When marriage is regarded as a convenient sexual arrangement within the law, and the spouse as a thing to be cast aside like a worn-out utensil when it has ceased to have any further use, how can anything but moral disintegration of the worst sort be avoided?

How can the family upon which all society is built continue to exist, and how can the innocent victims who are bereft of healthy family life be expected to develop as good human beings should?

The answer is that healthy development under such conditions is not to be expected; and if that is so, it is high time that we attended to the cause of the problem.

Parents must be educated for the task of educating their children. The basic task of making healthy human beings of their children should be the main profession of parents. It is a task in which the parents have a right to expect some assistance from the school, the community, and all other relevant agencies, but it is a task primarily and essentially for the parents.

Parent education is therefore a most urgent desideratum. Parents need renewed confidence in themselves, and they need to rely less upon outside educational agencies than they have been accustomed to in the past. There has been too much abdication of responsibility for the rearing of their children.

Ideally, no one can do the parents' job of loving, protecting, securing, and strengthening the personality of the child. Toward the achievement of better mental health and the restoration to a healthier existence for society as a whole, parent education offers a most promising approach.

4. *The Anxiety Makers*

Anxiety concerning sexual matters in the Western world has its origin in large part in the teachings of Christianity. These teachings left no aspect of Western culture uninfluenced. Not altogether unsurprisingly, the profession of medicine proved no more immune to this influence than other professions. Indeed, as Dr. Alex Comfort shows in his fascinating book *The Anxiety Makers*,[1] the medical profession has contributed substantially to the institutionalization of sexual anxiety. Hence, sexual anxiety must be added to the not inconsiderable calendar of iatrogenic disorders, that is, disorders produced by medical men. The propagation of virtue by physicians has from the days of the witch doctor forward been primed not so much by the principle of a healthy mind in a healthy body as by the expedient principle of least effort. It is a principle of behavior common to the generality of civilized mankind, and it is the chief reason why poor purblind humanity has not only permitted such havoc to be created in the world but has actively participated in its own progressive dissolution.

In the case of the medical profession, the least effort has taken the form of an uncritical acquiescence in the accepted mores, in their maintenance, defense, support, and transmission. In his privileged position as the presiding deity over the corporeal fate

[1] New York: Delta, 1969.

of his patients, the physician was often able to close the gap between the spiritual, ethical, bodily, or fleshly problems which bedeviled the individual. The Doctors of Medicine and the Doctors of Divinity worked closely together and often combined both offices in the same person. For many centuries the occupation of the physician was under the close surveillance of the church, the practice of medicine being permitted only upon the sufferance of the church. It is therefore not surprising that Doctors of Divinity and Doctors of Medicine should so often have found common cause in the propagation of the faith. Thus, in the Year of Grace 1967 the president of the American Medical Association, Milford O. Rouse, M.D., declared in his inaugural address that the concept of health was a privilege rather than a right.[2] A privilege, of course, vouchsafed only to those who are spiritually, in Dr. Rouse's terms, in a state of grace, that is, politically right-minded. I recommend his address to the reader as a cautionary homily on one man's view, at any rate, of the character of modern medical practice.

Since physicians were almost always males, their prejudices against "the weaker sex" were much in evidence. Hence, as the learned Ebenezer Sibly so conscientiously showed, the primary command of God being *"increase and multiply,"* He was hardly best served by suppressing the calls of nature, and since abstinence bred maladies, it was better to marry than to burn. If, however, one could not marry, the female, especially, could take a certain decoction, like that distilled from the leaves of the mugwort, bryony, and pennyroyal. Such a decoction constituted an infallible specific for whatever might otherwise ail the virtuous female. Principally the focus of attention was on preserving the health of the male, the female being considered expendable. Women were so easily disposed of because, unless they were utterly depraved, they were not supposed to have much sexual feeling. The effect of this kind of teaching was

2 *Journal of the American Medical Association*, Vol. 201 (July 17, 1967), pp. 169–75.

to make millions of women ill with guilt for experiencing what they had been led to believe were utterly wicked feelings. In the marital relation it was wrong for a woman to refuse her husband his "marital rights," since this would be detrimental to his health. The wife's health was not a consideration in the matter at all! However, sexual intercourse with his wife more often than once in ten days would ruin, it was held, a strong man's health, and for weaker men sex was only to be recommended at greater intervals. Premarital sex, being sinful, was of course also unhealthy.

William Acton's book *Functions and Disorders of the Reproductive Organs,* published in 1857, constitutes a ghastly museum of Victorian attitudes toward sex. These views are presented at length in Dr. Comfort's book. Virtue might be its own reward, but from the practical point of view it protected one from the dangers of vice. Hence, one was good not because it was virtuous to be so but because it was dangerous not to be. Intercourse during pregnancy was strictly forbidden by the anxiety makers because it led, so said the "authorities," to such dire results in the children as epilepsy, sexual precocity, and depravity.

The medicosexual history of masturbation presents perhaps the most curious cautionary example of medical anxiety making at its worst. In the secular literature up to the beginning of the eighteenth century masturbation seems to have excited no censorious interest whatever. If anything, it was considered a useful form of relief and an antidote against the dangerous allurements of women. The church had always considered it a sin to thus "abuse" oneself. And it was no accident that the work which initiated the frightful mythology about masturbation, *Onania, or the Heinous Sin of Self-pollution,* was written by an anonymous clergyman turned quack doctor. This awful work was published in 1710 and was given its most powerful endorsement by the devout Roman Catholic physician and hygienist Samuel Auguste Tissot, who in his own work, *Onanism: A Treatise on the Disorders Produced by Masturbation,* which appeared in 1758, served to scatter its nonsense far and wide. The ignorance, arrogance, and irresponsibility of the eighteenth- and nineteenth-century medical profession in matters sexual was staggering. No less a person than Benjamin Rush, in the first textbook on psychiatry to be published in the United States, wrote that masturbation produced "seminal weakness, impotence, dysury, tabes dorsalis, pulmonary consumption, dimness of sight, vertigo, epilepsy, hypochondriasis, loss of memory, manalgia, fatuity and death."

This plague of epidemic medical nonsense spread over the whole of the Western world, and in some regions persists to this day. There were a few who, like the hardheaded John Hunter, resisted the contagion of pathogenic ideas, but the majority embraced the "fact" of "masturbational insanity" with suspicious fervor. The truth is there was considerable profit for the quacks in this "heinous crime, this abominable sin," and they made the most of it. In wheedling and unctuous advertisements for their utterly spurious "remedies," the perfidious purveyors did a thriving business. Their huckstering methods were dreadful.

The centuries during which physicians drummed up public anxiety about sex and reproduction in order to frighten people into being good eventually paid off in hard cash—and in innumerable tragedies. The preoccupation with the sinfulness of sex led to the most awful excesses: clitoridectomies (female circumcision), hysterectomies, circumcision, and—this may be difficult for some readers to believe—even removal of the penis was in some cases recommended and surgically performed. Castration of the male was also carried out as a "cure" for masturbation.

The derangement of attitudes toward sex infected the most balanced of men, displacing and overriding science, logic, and experience. But, as Dr. Comfort has remarked, "The astounding resilience of human common sense against the anxiety makers is one of the really cheering aspects of history."

The concentration on sex for a time diverted attention from the other organs, but not for long. The rectum and anus, being so close to the organs of sex, were bound to suggest themselves as profitable avenues of approach to the anxiety makers. The ghastlinesses for which these ventrally motivated exploiters were responsible constitute a sorry chapter in the history of medical malpractice. Proceeding progressively onward and upward in the intestinal tract, all twenty-one feet of it, could hardly escape the redemptive zeal of the medical missionaries. The story of Sir Arbuthnot Lane, a mandarin of the English medical profession, on this errand bent constitutes an alarming example of the dangers of medical enthusiasm. Poisoning of the intestinal tract and the constipation of autointoxication that this was alleged to cause were simply disastrous, according to Lane, resulting in, among other things, tuberculosis and insanity. Surgical removal of the colon was Lane's way of "solving" the problem. He also prescribed paraffin with, as may well be imagined, the most unpleasant consequences. Lane is parodied in Shaw's *The Doctor's Dilemma.*

Have we changed much? It is greatly to be doubted. There are still innumerable doctors who upon sight of the tonsils recommend that they be removed without delay. Why? Are the reasons given by physicians for removing these valuable lymphoid organs any more soundly based than those given by the clitoridectomists not so long ago? Students at a certain university hospital in London will recall an eminent physician who held that since virtually all diseases began in the teeth he would see no patient until he had had all his teeth extracted or had promised to do so!

Many other physicians ordered all root-canal-therapied teeth or carious teeth extracted since they might be the source of the infection troubling the patient. In some cases this was in fact the source of an infection, but in most it was not; nevertheless, thousands of people lost perfectly good teeth—a tragedy in itself —because of this medical faddism.

Dentists, who tend to be much sounder and very much more practical scientists than medical men, have made the public sufficiently conscious, not anxious, about the importance of caring for one's teeth, and there has been an enormous improvement in the dental and general health of people.

In the nineteenth century there was nothing that could be called adequate teaching in the medical schools on matters sexual. There were some matters that it was considered could be left to the discretion of the physician when he got into practice. It was unnecessary to discuss such things in the course of his instruction. The attitude toward sex in the medical schools was not merely bigoted and obscurantist but also reactionary. Education in sex is still either nonexistent or appallingly inadequate in most medical schools today.

Nothing, however, could have been more astonishing than the reactionary resistance by the medical profession to birth control and the utter nonsense preached by the leading medical journals of the day against it. As in so many areas in which social advances might have been expected to come from the medical forum, here, too, they were instead initiated by laymen: Charles Bradlaugh and Annie Besant in England and Margaret Sanger in the United States.

The objection to birth control was based on the belief that such freedom from conception, when contraceptives were used, would put the female, as the *Lancet* said, in an editorial, "on an equal footing with an experienced prostitute." In short, birth control was most corrupting of human morals. It "is an evil and a disgrace," Professor J. W. Taylor told the British Gynaecology Society in 1904, "for it is undoubtedly to this that we must attribute not only the diminishing birth rate but the diminishing value of our population." [3]

Again, as was to be expected, today the anxiety makers are busily occupied with the dangers of the pill. But that, too, will

[3] *Lancet,* Vol. II (1904), p. 1843.

pass. It may well be that future generations will look back on those of us who believe that the pill is a population control device and consider us mistaken and misguided. I rather suspect not. Overenthusiastic perhaps, but not misguided. Population control is the number one problem of humanity. Unless that problem is solved, none of the other problems of humanity can be solved. Here, I believe, a great deal more anxiety will have to be generated before the dangers of overpopulation are sufficiently widely appreciated for the individual to be persuaded to do something about them.[4] Anxiety that leads to healthy concern and soundly based conduct is a desirable form of concern.

A society that puts its citizens in jail for possessing marihuana but freely permits them to possess guns creates anxieties on legalistic grounds about relatively unimportant matters and diverts attention from those important ones about which anxiety would be very much in order—smoking, for example.

The anxieties created by obstetricians concerning pregnancy and especially childbirth and those created by the pediatricians about children are still to some extent with us. These are matters worthy of separate studies. They would make valuable contributions toward the understanding and remedying of the human condition, for they would, properly executed, get to the root of a great deal of the disorder and personal disorganization that exists in the world today.

[4] Ashley Montagu, *Man Observed* (New York: Putnam's, 1968).

5. *The Kinsey Reports,* *Your Children, and You*

The Kinsey Reports consist of two volumes by Dr. Alfred C. Kinsey and his collaborators. These two volumes are *The Sexual Life of the Human Male,* published in January, 1948, and *The Sexual Life of the Human Female,* published in April, 1953. It is, I believe, true to say that no previous publications on this subject aroused such great interest among Americans as the Kinsey Reports. In spite of a great deal of prurient interest, which was largely disappointed, the effects of the Kinsey Reports have, on the whole, been salutary.[1]

In our society, in most societies of the Western world, sex has been endowed with an importance which has been exceeded only by the veil of mystery and ignorance with which it has been obscured. Were this not the case, the Kinsey Reports would probably never have been written or, having been written, might have been read by only comparatively few experts. As it is, the subject of sex has for so long been treated as something that decent people do not talk about that, indeed, it has

---

[1] The book which aroused almost as great an interest as the Kinsey volumes, *Human Sexual Response* (Boston: Little, Brown & Co., 1966) by William H. Masters and Virginia E. Johnson, is somewhat differently oriented, and in many ways more valuable.

for that very reason become for many persons an "indecent" subject which only "indecent" persons discuss.

Fortunately, this attitude toward sex is crumbling, but the ancient and heavy fog of obscurantist ways of thinking about sex is still, to some extent, with us. It was Jonathan Swift who remarked that when we go about creating a man we draw the sheet and snuff the candle, but when we go about killing a man we carry the instrument of destruction upon our shoulder for all the world to see! The result of the proscription of any open discussion of sex has been the production of more ignorance, ineptitude, mental and physical illness, and general unhappiness than could possibly be traced to any other single cause. One cannot begin to measure the load of guilt, anguish, and misery from which human beings have suffered in consequence of the taboo upon the discussion of sex. The response to the Kinsey Reports, the response to almost any publication that has anything to do with sex, is surely an indication of the hunger for information which so many find themselves in need of. It is often said that much of this interest is of a salacious kind. Possibly it is, but that very fact should constitute a further evidence of the fact that many people are confused and desperately in need of help. The person who has an informed healthy attitude toward sex cannot think in anything but healthy terms about it.

The discussion of sex needs to be brought out into the light of day, and the first thing most of us need to learn are the facts about social behavior in our own society. Toward this end the Kinsey Reports constitute a significant contribution. How do the Kinsey Reports affect your children? Your children will undoubtedly have heard a great deal about the Kinsey Reports. It is highly improbable that they will have read them, though it is not unlikely that they will have read one or more of the numerous, and usually quite reliable, magazine articles on them. There are many surprising, even astonishing, and certainly controversial things in the Kinsey Reports. There are some things in these books which I believe some authorities will consider unsound. How are parents to benefit most from the Kinsey Reports, and how may parents best meet the questions that adolescents of the Kinsey and post-Kinsey Age are likely to put to them, either in so many words or in so many acts?

I should think that one of the first prerequisites is for parents to familiarize themselves with the Kinsey Reports. Many parents will be unable to do this, but with the spate of magazine articles and inexpensive but excellent paperback books—such as the Signet special *About The Kinsey Report* (New York: New American Library, 1948) and *An Analysis of the Kinsey Reports* (New York: New American Library, 1954)—it should be quite a simple matter to acquaint oneself with the essential facts contained in the Kinsey Reports as well as with the important and enlightening criticisms of them. There is nothing more impressive to one's children than the confidence which comes to them from the feeling that their parents know what they are talking about. If, on the other hand, you are going to talk out of the depths of your prejudices and ignorance of the facts as discussed by Kinsey, his commentators, and his critics, you are unlikely to be of much help to your children.

Kinsey has made available a large number of facts which should be immensely helpful to parents in connection with the education and development of their children. Parents should pay Kinsey the tribute and do themselves and their children the service of acquainting themselves with what he has to say. For example, Kinsey points out that in his sample of 5,940 women, no matter of what religion, the more devoutly they were brought up the less likely they were to indulge in premarital relations. If one believes that, in our society at least, premarital relations are on the whole undesirable, the importance of a healthy religious training in childhood should be obvious. What is a healthy religious training? It is essentially a training in *love* and *relatedness*. I use two words which here mean the same thing. Love of God, love of one's parents and relatives, love of one's fellow human beings, love of nature, love of life, and relatedness to all of them. Not that God is love, but that love is God. The production of such an attitude of mind in one's children should be the principal task of education, and in this sense all education should be religious. Religion is the recognition of the fact that we are all responsible to a power outside ourselves to keep the faith and the power within ourselves. The point need not be pressed. If children are brought up to be good human beings they will not need to be taught much else. In our society we tend to place too much emphasis on the teaching of subjects and not enough on the teaching of human beings. Religion is not a subject, nor is education—each should amount to the same thing: a way of life. Parents and teachers can combine forces to provide this for our children. The challenge to do so is there. Who will take it up?

Kinsey found that females who had had premarital relations reached orgasm during the first year of marriage more often than females who had not had premarital relations. Kinsey all but says that if women would be sexually successful in marriage they ought to indulge in premarital relations. At any rate, this is the conclusion that many of his readers have drawn from his discussion of this matter. Kinsey himself appears to be very impressed by his figures and his charts, but here he almost certainly puts the chart before the horse. As many critics of Kinsey have pointed out, the women who were orgasmically more successful in the first year of marriage were probably so not because of their premarital experiences but because of other possible personality factors. Such women may have been less "tied up," had fewer "hang-ups," than the others, been less inhibited in general—and a thousand and one other things. Kinsey has committed the elementary error of assuming that because two things are associated one is necessarily the cause of the other.

Whether premarital relations are desirable or not must, I think, be decided on grounds other than the Kinsey findings. A mature approach to this question begins with the first principle of maturity, that is, the ability to postpone immediate satisfactions for long-term goals. Premarital relations indulged merely in order to obtain immediate pleasures make sex an end instead of a means—a means to enduring happiness in an enduring relationship with a member of the opposite sex. Because in our society we have overemphasized the importance of sex by hedging it about with prohibitions and mystery, we have converted it into something to be sought after as an end in itself, to be indulged in for the forbidden pleasures it yields, whereas sex is no more an end in itself than is breathing. In the case of breathing it is obvious to everyone that it is a means of keeping alive. It is perhaps less obvious to many that we eat in order to live, for many persons behave as if they live in order to eat. It is, of course, quite happily possible to combine the two attitudes, and most people in fact do, though many others pay the price of overeating in the disorders incident to that practice. To make eating an end in life can lead only to disaster. One should eat reasonably. Similarly, one should deal with sex reasonably, making it not an end but a means to a fuller, happier life. There is every reason to believe that in our society such a life is best achieved by those who have learned how to postpone immediate satisfactions for long-term ones. This is a universal truth, but it is particularly true of sex relations.

Just as one should avoid making too much of sex, one should avoid making too little of it. Sex is a precious gift. One should respect it and neither cheapen nor abuse it. Those who make of sex an end are likely to make marriage a means to an end—sex. Those who do so are marrying for the wrong reasons—their marriages will rarely be successful. The only enduring basis for marriage is character. The greatest gift one can bring one's spouse is not one's sexual attractiveness but one's character.

Kinsey finds that males are sexually very much more easily aroused than females. Parents should avail themselves of this piece of information in a creatively useful manner. It is a fact, and it is an important one. It is important for parents to explain this difference and its meaning to their teen-age children. Girls particularly need to understand that because of the male's much easier sexual excitability his apparently intense interest in a girl may be little more than the expression of his more easily aroused sexual desire. Both boys and girls should be taught to understand that a sexual interest in a member of the opposite sex is not the same thing as love, that both girls and boys frequently honestly mistake such a sexual interest for the "real thing." There undoubtedly is such a thing as love at first sight, but there is assuredly such a thing also as repentance at leisure. Usually one has to learn to know another person, and that takes time. An intense "rush" usually means little more than that. It can, of course, constitute a beginning—but it should never be mistaken for the end—which is love. Boys and girls not only need to be good about such matters; they also need to be careful. They need to understand each other better than they at present do, so that they may respond more understandingly, helpfully, and constructively to each other's problems.

Attraction between boys and girls of teen age can be a beautiful and inspiring experience. It should be viewed and treated tenderly. Adolescence is the most misunderstood period of human development, and the most trying for the suffering adolescent. Teen-agers require all the sympathetic understanding they can get. Misguided notions on the part of parents as to the "proper" age at which girls can be allowed to be interested in boys, and vice versa, should be strictly out of order. If children are respected and loved by their parents, the children will thereby learn to respect and love their parents, themselves, and others. Doubtless at the present time these constitute, for many parents, counsels of perfection, for in spite of their best-intentioned efforts they have not adequately loved or respected their children. For such parents the best counsel that one can give is that it is never too late to start respecting and loving one's children.

Finally, I cannot too strongly emphasize the importance of a sense of humor for parents at this time, when parents are inclined to take their children overseriously.

6. *Where Kinsey Went Wrong*

Does love exist? One wouldn't know it from Dr. Kinsey's report on 5,940 women. Does motherhood in any way influence the sexual behavior of American women? One couldn't tell from the Kinsey Report. At least, Dr. Kinsey has nothing explicitly to report on the subject. For Dr. Kinsey, sexual activity is a matter of "biological performance." I am afraid he couldn't be more wrong.

Sexual activity may be nothing more than "biological performance" in insects. In human beings it is a social, psychological, and often spiritual performance as well. Sexual activity in human beings represents not simply our nature but our second nature—what we have learned to make of what we are.

As is well known, our sexual life is more sensitive to psychological stimulation than almost any other form of human behavior. And yet psychological facts about the women questioned in *Sexual Behavior of the Human Female* are conspicuously lacking.

How many of Dr. Kinsey's 5,940 women enjoyed a "normal" psychological development? To what extent and in what directions did many or any of them undergo experiences in early life which influenced or distorted their later sexual activities? What was the nature of these experiences? We do not know, for Dr. Kinsey doesn't tell us. Nor can Dr. Kinsey be excused on the ground that he is interested only in sexual behavior, not in what *caused* the sexual behavior of the women he interviewed. He *is* interested in causes, as he himself says in the opening paragraph of the book. "It has been," he writes, "a fact-finding survey in which an attempt has been made to discover what people do sexually, *and* what factors may account for their patterns of sexual behavior...."

As it turns out, however, the "factors" on the basis of which Dr. Kinsey offers to explain human sexual behavior are almost entirely physical factors. They are the same kind of factors one might expect to find in studying the sexual behavior of ants or beetles. And as a matter of fact, before he turned to the sexual behavior of human beings Dr. Kinsey's specialty *was* the study of insects (entomology), a field in which he is a leading authority and one in which he has done distinguished work for many years. In bringing the methods involved in insect study to the study of human beings, Kinsey indulges in a familiar scientific fallacy—sometimes known as the "nothing but" fallacy. This is the notion that human beings can be reduced to a kind of mechanical organism, that they are "nothing but" rather complicated machines.

Although Kinsey refers with respect to human emotions in the first few pages of his book, it becomes obvious as he proceeds that emotions to him are primarily the *results* of sexual activity rather than being in any way involved in the *causes* of this activity. "Too many husbands," he says at one point, "fail to comprehend that their wives are not aroused as they [the husbands] are in the anticipation of a sexual relationship, and fail to comprehend that their wives may need general physical stimulation before they are sufficiently aroused to want genital union or completed coitus." And again, "It is possible that orgasm which is accompanied by a pulse running at 150 may be more stimulating than orgasm which is reached with pulse running at 100 or so."

One could hardly go further in the insectification of human beings, it seems to me, than in the second statement. The first passage is quite literally the nearest Kinsey approaches to the realization that emotional factors play some role in a wife's sexual responses to her husband. It is unbelievable, but it is true.

Here is a book which is concerned with the sexual behavior of human beings, and in particular with the sexual behavior of the female—a creature naturally designed to love and mother the human species—yet neither love nor motherhood is even so much as mentioned! The word "love" occurs once, and this in a footnote (number 11, page 366); "motherhood" occurs not at all. It is not enough for Kinsey to say: "Nothing we have said or may subsequently say . . . should be construed to mean that we are unaware of the importance of psychologic factors in human sexual behavior." We want some evidence of it. I fail to find any evidence in this huge tome, *The Sexual Behavior of the Human Female,* consisting of 842 closely printed pages, that Kinsey and his coauthors have anywhere really understood the meaning of a human emotion in their 5,940 women.

The entomological approach is everywhere apparent throughout the book, but nowhere more so than when Kinsey comes to deal with what he calls *psychological* factors. Here, we say to ourselves, he will at long last get around to the emotions. But what a letdown, and what a surprise, is in store for us! At best, and one has to work very hard to find it, one learns that most of the women in the Kinsey sample have worried a great deal about sex. They worry about the effects of premarital intercourse on their chances of happiness in marriage. They worry about masturbation, frigidity, chastity, homosexuality. They worry about their own performance in their sexual relations with their husbands, and they worry about his performance in relation to themselves. They seek reassurance that they are not so different from other women. The background of these worries or the effect of the worries on actual sexual behavior is not considered important.

Also unfortunately, Kinsey seems to confuse "psychological stimulation" with "emotion." In the sixteenth chapter, "Psychologic Factors in Sexual Response," for example, he says, "It has sometimes been suggested that the male's capacity to be erotically aroused by *any* female, and even by a physically, mentally, and aesthetically unattractive, lower level prostitute, is a demonstration of the fact that he is not as dependent as females are upon psychologic factors for the achievement of satisfactory sexual relationships." If the term "psychologic factor" means anything, here it certainly seems to refer to the female's *personal, emotional* response toward a sexual partner. And yet immediately following this passage, Kinsey goes on to say, "On the contrary, the capacity of many males to respond to *any* type of female is actually a demonstration of the fact that psychologic conditioning, rather than the physical or the psychologic stimuli that are immediately present, is the chief source of his erotic response. As far as his psychologic responses are concerned, the male in many instances may not be having coitus with the immediate sexual partner, but with all of the other girls with whom he has ever had coitus, and with the entire genus Female with which he would like to have coitus."

In other words, men can be erotically aroused *without emotion* by a whole host of stimuli to which they have become conditioned, whereas women seldom can.

How unfortunate the results of Kinsey's own lack of clarity can be is already apparent from the misinterpretations which have appeared in the press on just this point. To take but one example, the *Herald Tribune* (August 31, 1953, p. 6), reporting Kinsey, writes: "Essentially, it is the male who is more powerfully moved by psychologic stimuli and through his emotions than the female, who responds more to physical stimulation."

This is the exact opposite of the truth and of Kinsey's actual findings! Incidentally, this passage forcefully illustrates the serious misunderstandings to which Kinsey's own failure to distinguish sharply between "psychologic stimulation" and "emotion" give rise. "Psychosexual stimulation" and "emotion" are two different things, as Kinsey recognizes when he points out that his "data indicates that the average female marries to establish a home, to establish a long-time affectional relationship with a single spouse, and to have children whose welfare may become the prime business of her life. . . . Most males would admit that all of these are desirable aspects of a marriage . . . it is probable that few males would marry if they did not anticipate that they would have an opportunity to have coitus regularly with their wives."

The truth is, as Kinsey's findings abundantly show, that for the men he has studied almost anything associated with sex is psychosexually stimulating. As particular examples of what stimulates men psychosexually, he cites nude figures, erotic stories, burlesque, and observation of sexual action. Women, he points out, are seldom erotically responsive to any of these things. They are, however, very much affected "erotically" by "literary materials." This highly significant fact the Kinsey investigators find quite baffling. "We do not clearly understand," they write, "why this should be so. There are possible psychoanalytic interpretations, but in view of all the evidence that there may be basic neurophysiologic differences between females and males, we hesitate to offer any explanation of the present data." One would have thought that the special *emotional* appeal of these "literary materials"—about which Kinsey tells us absolutely nothing—particularly if they were of a romantic nature, would be a sufficient explanation. In a footnote Kinsey does point out that others have drawn attention to the fact that females often find erotic stimulation in reading romantic stories or seeing movies. Is it possible that "romance" means something more to the average female than it does to the average male? And that the response of the female to "romance" is essentially a matter of *emotion?* Judging from facts like this, is it not perhaps the *female* who is "more powerfully moved" through her emotions than the male in sexual matters?

Another important and dangerously misleading aspect of the Kinsey book is the material on premarital relations. "Among those," Kinsey writes, "who had had pre-marital coitus but had failed to reach orgasm in that coitus, between 38 and 56 per cent had failed to reach orgasm in their first year of marriage. But among the females who had pre-marital coitus in which they had reached orgasm at least twenty-five times before marriage, only 3 per cent had failed to achieve some orgasm during the first year of marriage."

Kinsey draws the somewhat illogical conclusion from facts like this that if the prohibitions upon premarital sexual relations were relaxed there would be a great improvement in the sexual health of both sexes.

I think this is debatable, especially in the context of Kinsey's own findings. Kinsey's subjects were volunteers. That very fact suggests that most of them could be properly described as belonging to the more sophisticated and sexually unconventional part of the population. Indeed, Dr. A. H. Maslow, in studying a group of girls who had volunteered to act as interviewees for Kinsey, found that they were predominantly of this kind. Clearly, such girls would more frequently tend toward premarital sexual behavior of a kind which girls of less sophistication and more conventional habits would tend to avoid.

The fact that the females who had experienced premarital sexual relations with men—petting or coitus—and achieved orgasm are more likely to achieve sexual satisfaction in the marriage relationship does not necessarily mean that premarital intercourse has anything to do with good sex relations in marriage. It may well be that the temperament of the girl who indulges in premarital relations is sufficient to explain her freer sexual adjustment in marriage, and that premarital intercourse with or without orgasm plays no such role as Kinsey assumes it does. This Kinsey is willing to admit as a possibility, for he writes: "The most responsive females may have been the ones who had had the largest amount of pre-marital experience, and because they were responsive, they were the ones who had most often reached orgasm in marriage." But he doesn't think it is the whole story. Maybe it isn't. I think it not improbable that it constitutes the greater part of the whole story.

It seems to me that what has escaped Kinsey and his co-workers is that sexual adjustment in marriage is largely an expression of the same factors which enable one to adjust successfully in any human relationship. This is basically the conclusion of Professor Lewis M. Terman's classic study *Psychological Factors in Marital Happiness* (1938). "The qualities of personality that predispose a person to happiness or unhappiness in his relations with others," in Terman's words, are the qualities which appeared to be the most conspicuously important in the success or failure of the marriages investigated by Terman and his associates. Terman states the important conclusion: "Our data do not confirm the view so often heard that the key to happiness in marriage is nearly always to be found in sexual compatibility. They indicate, instead, that the influence of the sexual factors is at most no greater than that of the combined personality and background factors, and that it is probably less." And this is the conclusion of most modern students of marriage.

What our society needs is not more "sex education" in the form of premarital intercourse, but more and better education in human relations. Sexual behavior is not and should not be what it has become, a particular and sequestrated form of behavior which requires separate handling in the education of the human being. On the contrary, sexual relationships are part and parcel of human relationships, and the development of the

person's sexual capacities should be considered as an insepa-
rable part of his total development as a person. The latter
process must consist principally in the development of the
human being's potentialities to love and be loved. A mentally
healthy adjusted wife, like a mentally healthy adjusted husband,
is the work, primarily, of a good mother in a really satisfactory
healthy mother-child relationship.

Were we, as parents, to love our children as they should be
loved, problems of marital adjustment would be reduced, I am
sure, to a minimum. It is at this basic level of parent-child
relationships that, I believe most authorities agree, the problems which Kinsey believes will be solved by greater premarital
license will in fact be solved. It is, I think, due to Kinsey's fundamental misunderstanding of the nature of human nature and
the role which emotions play in human development that he
has fallen into grievous error here.

Structured as our society is, premarital sexual relations often
lead to disastrous consequences—perhaps not so often in the
women of Kinsey's sample but certainly in too many girls in the
general population. Our attitudes toward premarital indiscre-
tions have certainly become more humane, and that is all to
the good, but that is not equivalent to saying that our society
can or should encourage premarital sexual relationships. When
we have developed sufficient human maturity, the problem of
premarital sexual activities will perhaps not arise, because the
sexual behavior of the person will be a function of a mature
mind and society itself will have reached that level of maturity
which will enable it to agree that the sexual behavior of the
person is his own affair, and insofar as it is in no way damaging
either to himself or to anyone else, it is entirely a private matter.

One final point must certainly be made in any critical discussion of the Kinsey book, and that is the misleading nature of
its title, *Sexual Behavior in the Human Female*. Actually the
book is representative of neither the human nor the American

female, for it deals only with a limited geographic sample of American women drawn largely from cities and towns, 75 percent of whom went to college as compared with only 7.5 percent of women in the general population who had gone to college. Only 25 percent of women drawn from the general population are represented in Kinsey's sample, while of the 3.7 percent who never got beyond grade school Kinsey's sample has only 3 percent. Only 181 of the total number of 5,940 women were from the lower economic levels.

As for geographic distribution, only the following states are represented: New York, New Jersey, Pennsylvania, Massachusetts, Illinois, Indiana, Ohio, Maryland, Florida, and California.

Clearly, both the education and the geographic sampling are certainly nonrepresentative of women in the United States as a whole.

Furthermore, religious samplings are not truly representative, nor are sufficiently fine distinctions made between early religious training and present religious attitude. Since religious devoutness and undevoutness are apparently important factors in sexual behavior, as Kinsey himself shows, the unrepresentativeness of his religious samples introduces a serious distorting factor. In other words, the larger the number of undevout women in the sample, the more frequently is unconventional behavior likely to be encountered, and since Kinsey's sample is heavily weighted toward the undevout side of the scale, one may readily perceive how unrepresentative that sample is.

As was to be expected, the volume on women is a much more human document than that on the men, but the best that Kinsey can do with human emotions is to state that they exist; he can neither measure nor analyze them, and he gets as far away from the unremembered psychological conditions which were undoubtedly operative in influencing his subjects' sexual behavior as he possibly can—for he is, in fact, a pollster rather than a student of human beings.

An anonymous poet sums it up rather well:

> O cupid! Cast away your bow and quiver—
>   Statistics prove your method inexact.
> O Donne! Go take a jump into the river:
>   You hymned the essence but ignored the fact.
> Locked in some cool aseptic heaven above,
>   Trained statisticians painlessly inquire
> Into the quaint geometry of love,
>   The quantitative aspects of desire;
> Observe the conduct of the lovesick male
>   (Not passionate, not noble, not obscene),
> And plot it on a logarithmic scale,
>   Noting a random scatter round the mean.
> O monumental volume, smug and fat!
>   Did man, who wrote the Song of Songs, write that?
> O God! O Kinsey! O Jehoshaphat!

7. *Understanding Our Sexual Desires*

It is a curious thing that of all the most highly energized needs of man the only one that is not necessary for his survival is the one which gives him the most trouble. In order to live it is necessary to breathe, to eat and drink, to eliminate, to be active, and to rest. If *all* these needs are not satisfied, death follows very rapidly. But sexual intercourse, between male and female, a necessity for the survival of the group, is not in the least necessary as far as the survival of the individual is concerned. The person can live for long stretches of time or permanently without sexual relations of any kind and not suffer the least biological injury.

How, then, does it come about that man, in the Western world, is so much preoccupied with, even bedeviled by, his sexual irritations? *Sexual Behavior in the Human Male* goes a long way toward answering that question.

Whether or not the sampling techniques, upon which the whole value of the statistical analysis depends, are sound makes not one iota of difference to the fact which is repeatedly highlighted throughout the book—namely, that the moral values, the attitudes of the class to which one belongs and the overall moral values of one's society determine the character of the person's sexual behavior.

It is now quite clear that how a person behaves sexually is largely determined not by inborn factors but by learning. What heredity supplies is a certain common fund of sexual energy, the physiological surgency of which varies at different ages and at different times. What the process of being turned into a socialized human being does is to cause the individual to *acquire* certain *ways* of behavior in relation to sex. The *way* of sexual behavior which the person acquires depends largely on the experiences to which he is exposed in a particular series of social groups, the family, playmates, the school, church, reading matter, movies, and the like. If any of these educational agents are irrational, moralistic, pornographic, prudish, or otherwise defective in their approach to sexual matters, this will be reflected in the behavior of those who have been exposed to them. It did not take the Kinsey Report to make us aware of the defectiveness of our present practices in the sexual education of the person. We have been aware of that for a long time. What *Sexual Behavior in the Human Male* does is to point up the absurdities and inefficiencies of our institutional controls.

Our social attitudes toward sexual behavior stem, as Kinsey and his colleagues point out, from moral codes and laws of Assyrian, Babylonian, Hebraic, and even earlier origins. Certainly our institutionalized or accepted ways of thinking on this subject lag far behind the realities of the knowledge we possess today. If Kinsey's book does no more than make the proportions of this gap clear it will have justified all the labor that has been put into it.

What this work does so well is to demonstrate the fact that man's preoccupation with sex and its taboos is largely due to the maximization of interest created in the subject because society gives it a maximum amount of repressive attention. By devoting so much opposed attention to its control, and by doing so in a manner totally disregarding the realities of the facts, society creates high focal points of pressure within the person. Such pressures represent the accumulated tension of needs which have been forbidden by society. In other words, society controls the expression of sexual needs in such a way as to maximize their value out of all proportion to their biological or psychological importance. This is not to suggest that social controls of sexual behavior are unnecessary. In fact, such controls will always be necessary. It is, however, meant to suggest that the present controls are out of touch with modern knowledge. The result of this is that we continue to bring up children in the most distorted of ways, especially in the matter of sexual education, so that between the inhibited female and the libidinous male (or vice versa), who have picked up what they know of sex in the most haphazard way, there is no great cause for wonder that marriage has become so fragile an institution.

Concerning the meaning, the art, and the science of sex, men and women in our culture are woefully ignorant. I think the probabilities are high that the Kinsey Reports and their analyses, together with the discussions to which they will give rise, will alter all this—very much for the better.

Nearly three quarters of a century has passed since the appearance of the first volume of Havelock Ellis' *Studies in the Psychology of Sex: Sexual Inversion*. In that same year (1898), an English court declared the book a "lewd wicked bawdy scandalous and obscene libel" and ordered its seizure and destruction. As Ellis wrote forty years later, "By the method which Order and Respectability closed to me, my books would perhaps have sold by the dozen; by the method Order and Respectability compelled me to adopt they have sold, and continue today to sell steadily, on a far larger scale, in an ever-increasing circle around the world." [1]

Studies in the Psychology of Sex became, indeed, an epoch-making work; epoch-making in the sense that it substantially altered the views of the several generations for whom it threw a flood of light upon what had hitherto been the dark arcanum

[1] Havelock Ellis, *My Life* (Boston: Houghton Mifflin, 1939), p. 368.

of the unmentionable—sex. Alone and unaided, and completely
without support, Ellis carried the work to seven scholarly volumes which inspired a host of other researchers to explore more
deeply a subject which Order and Respectability had decreed
as unmentionable. The advent of Freud and the development
of the psychoanalytic movement, together with the tremendous
changes brought about by World War I, accelerated the acceptance and free discussion of sex to the point at which after World
War II an inquiry such as *Sexual Behavior in the Human Male*
became possible.

With the publication of this work the pioneer labor of Ellis
reaches its second phase of development, the phase of intensive
statistical investigation of the various segments of the population of a single country. The social effects of this new research
are undoubtedly going to be quite as considerable as were those
produced by the publication of Ellis' great work. Within three
months of publication the book had already climbed high on
the best-seller lists, and it has been beyond doubt the most discussed book, in the United States at least, of its time. Hence
it might be well to consider some of the likely changes which
the publication of the projected twenty volumes will bring
about.

Before considering this aspect of the subject, which will have
to be based on the first of the twenty volumes, there are several
points I should like to discuss here with a view to setting the
record straight.

When the authors point out that "the histories of persons
born and raised in Continental Europe usually involve a great
deal of extramarital intercourse," it is quite evident that they
are aware of the importance of national and cultural differences in determining sexual behavior. It would have been well
had they made this point more explicit.

The most stupendous fallacy which runs through the whole
work is the authors' implied assumption that the normal is
equatable with a large number. They do not put this in so

many words, but the interpretation which they give to their findings takes the following form: It was hitherto thought that a particular form of behavior was relatively rare; it was therefore considered abnormal and undesirable. We now know that it is very frequent and would probably be much more frequent if it were not tabooed; a form of behavior which is so frequent cannot be abnormal; therefore it is normal. Let me illustrate with the actual words of the authors. The authors find that between the beginning of adolescence and old age, 37 percent of males have had some homosexual experience. Under the heading "Scientific and Social Implications," they write:

> In view of the data which we now have on the incidence and frequency of the homosexual, and in particular on its co-existence with the heterosexual in the lives of a considerable portion of the male population, it is difficult to maintain the view that psychosexual reactions between individuals of the same sex are rare and therefore abnormal or unnatural, or that they constitute within themselves evidence of neuroses or even psychoses.

The implication here is that such behavior is not abnormal but normal. The authors are careful not to give the appearance of sanctioning any of the forms of behavior they describe. But since, in America, *quantity* constitutes a moral value which makes acceptable and normalizes what in lesser quantities would be unacceptable and abnormal, the conclusion most likely to be drawn is that what has hitherto been thought unacceptable and abnormal must now be accepted and regarded as normal. After all, 6.3 million adult males with homosexual tendencies constitute a pretty sizable group. But then, so do the millions of persons with criminal tendencies in the United States, but their mere quantity makes them neither normal nor natural. Homosexuality, like the commission of a crime or an addiction to tobacco, is practically always an effect of certain types of cultural experience or conditioning. All these forms of behavior are acquired, *learned,* as the result of certain kinds of experience. Not one of them is natural, and whether one considers homosexuality, crime, or smoking normal or abnormal forms of behavior depends not on biological points of reference for one's judgment but on social criteria. As the authors write, "The way in which each group reacts to a particular sort of history determines the 'normality' or 'abnormality' of the individual's behavior—in that particular group."

The social criteria of this society have always been, and we may predict will always continue to be, that homosexuality is an abnormal form of behavior. Expert knowledge supports this judgment by showing that early conditioning factors in the life of the child are responsible for the development of homosexuality in the vast majority of cases. Society is responsible for the manner in which such persons were conditioned, and any society which withholds the knowledge from parents that would render such development impossible owes a double obligation to the family and the individual in taking an enlightened view of the position of the homosexual. But this is a very different thing from normalizing a condition which has developed as a result of experiences which in effect are productive of an incomplete human being—incomplete in the sense of not being fully able to participate in human relations and in the perpetuation of the species. In this sense, by biological, psychological, and social criteria homosexuality *is* unequivocally an abnormality whenever and wherever it occurs in human societies. Quantitative frequency cannot normalize it from the biological standpoint, no matter what the social viewpoint may be, in any society. I agree with the authors when they write, "If all persons with any trace of homosexual history, or those who were predominantly homosexual, were eliminated from the population today, there is no reason for believing that the incidence of the homosexual in the next generation would be materially reduced." But I would point out that this statement remains true only as long as the present ignorance of the factors causing homosexuality remains as widespread as it is today. Let every potential and actual parent learn what those factors are, and act accordingly, and homosexuality would be reduced to the vanishing point.

The authors are far from being unaware of the importance of social factors in the production of the homosexual, for they point out that social ostracism following perhaps a single and often fortuitous homosexual contact, the effect of community gossip, the behavior of judges, and administrators of penal, mental, and even academic institutions may play a determining role. Understanding this, I think the overemphasis on the inherited or biological factor implicit in the final sentences of the chapter is somewhat unfortunate. "The homosexual," the authors write, "has been a significant part of human sexual activity ever since the dawn of history, primarily because it is an expression of capacities that are basic in the human animal." If the authors' view is correctly or incorrectly interpreted to mean that homosexual capacities are part of the biological structure of drives with which the human animal is born, then this interpretation of the facts can be shown to be incorrect.

What the human animal is born with are the substrates of a sex drive which are quite undifferentiated. The differentiation of that drive is a matter very largely of social training, and that training may be of the most indirect kind. For example, children are sometimes brought up under family conditions which cause the child to identify himself very strongly with one or the other parent or to hate one or the other parent. These conditions may in themselves be sufficient to direct the child's sexual interest exclusively to members of his own sex.[2]

Under the usual conditions of family experience such responses do not develop, though other extrafamilial experiences may direct the child's interest into homosexual channels. In the

[2] For case history after case history in which such factors were operative, see G. W. Henry, *Sex Variants: A Study of Homosexual Patterns* (2 vols. New York: Paul B. Hoeber, 1941).

absence of such conditions, the pattern of heterosexual conditionings leads to the development of primarily heterosexual interests. These are not matters of conjecture but matters of fact. In short, sexual behavior, like any other form of behavior, is largely conditioned by the way in which the person has been socialized, that is, turned into a social human being. The capacity here of relevance which is basic in the human animal is its undifferentiated sex drive. How that capacity will be expressed will depend, with very few possible exceptions, upon the social experience to which the individual is exposed during his education as a human being. Hence, by adapting our educative procedures to the improvement of human personality in the light of our accumulated knowledge we can create a human being to almost any desired pattern. It is because the Kinsey Report raises questions which will lead to enlightening answers along these lines that its importance is so great.

The social consequences of the book are likely to be more numerous and more complex than I shall be able to consider here; almost without exception I believe that they will be greatly beneficial. Whoever reads the book cannot fail to obtain a deeper and more human understanding of the nature of the sexual. The statistics may interest or shock, but they will on the whole, together with the discussion of them by the authors, leave most persons with a more complete understanding of what it is to be human. They will realize that they are a part of a great company of human beings who are very like themselves; that what they were hitherto convinced were forms of behavior restricted to a relatively few persons including, or not, themselves is characteristic of a very large number of their fellow human beings.

The load of guilt which many persons have carried as a secret burden of their own will in many cases be lifted from them to the mutual advantage of themselves and their fellows. Understanding themselves better, they will more easily forgive instead of condemning both themselves and others, and hence their sense of guilt will no longer seek to expend itself in the form of hostility toward themselves and toward others. I do not say that this will happen in all cases. It will undoubtedly happen in some, and that "some" is likely to be a large and increasing number.

Where greater understanding has been produced there is likely to be greater sympathy, and where there is sympathy a just appraisal of behavior is more likely to obtain. Hence, we may look forward to a rapid acceleration of the movement toward more intelligent sex education. Since sex education involves education, to some extent at least, in human relations, we may look forward to very profitable advances in this direction. Specifically, the finding that the American male is most sexually active in the late teens will force a reconsideration of our attitudes toward premarital intercourse, the ineffectiveness of our social controls, the desirability of their modification, and the form which such modification might take.

A vast amount of misinformation and superstition relating to the sexual generally is exposed by Kinsey *et al.* and given the quietus of a corrective. This cannot help but have the most beneficial effect. It is not only the layman who will benefit from these corrections but also the physician. Greater perspective will be given to the physician who customarily sees a highly selected group of persons suffering from disorders which are by no means as infrequent as he usually thinks.

The emphasis which the authors give to their finding that "the psychologic bases of behavior [are] even more important than the biologic heritage and acquirements," and the weight of the evidence which supports this conclusion, will make it much easier to convince those who need convincing that it is through education and education alone that healthier sexual development and adjustment can be brought about.

Even though this volume deals with the male, it is quite apparent that the usual sexual education which the female receives in our society renders her quite as unprepared to live a healthy sexual life as the male. The female is vastly more inhibited than the male. The demands of the mores are such as to make the sexual, for the female in particular, something which is permissible only after marriage. The result of this taboo is that the sexual inhibitions of premarital life are carried over into married life. Add to this the usual thoroughly inadequate education of the male in the technique of sex relations, and a situation develops which would be comic were it not in reality tragic.

The marital unhappiness which arises from the male's inability to understand the nature of the female, and the inability of the female to adjust herself to the sexual demands of the male, is incalculably great, and again emphasizes the pressing necessity of a policy of enlightened sex education. Too long have the errors of superstition exercised their unhappy effects upon civilized man, with the resulting personal and social disorganization which is so well brought out in the pages of the Kinsey Report. The price of ignorance is far too great, the toll it takes in human lives and happiness too stupendous, to contemplate or tolerate.

The authors' proof of the significant differences in sexual outlet and its frequency in the different social groups of class, education, and religion again points up this importance of education in molding the sexual behavior of the person. Hence, I do not think it is too optimistic to expect that our outlook on sex education will undergo very substantial modification. That sex education will be commenced as early as the kindergarten level, and continued through all the grades of school and the college years, is not too much to expect. I feel very sure that it will come about, and at least in part as a result of the added impetus which the discussion of the Kinsey Report will give to a movement which has already been under way for some time.

8. *Kinsey on the American Female*

The Kinsey Reports on the male and female are important books, for Americans at any rate, because they have been and will continue to be responsible for a great deal of discussion concerning subjects which are not too frequently freely and openly discussed. Kinsey supplies the data which may serve as so many whetstones upon which to sharpen our ideas concerning the various aspects of sexual life in which we are involved as individuals and members of society. If only for this reason, Kinsey and his co-workers would deserve our gratitude. But the Kinsey workers have put us in their debt for many more reasons than this, and especially because they have thrown so much light upon certain fundamental differences which exist in the sexual nature of female and male. Our society and the persons constituting it will ultimately benefit greatly as a direct result of the publication of these reports. For the Kinsey Reports are likely to produce greater understanding and wisdom concerning the sexual behavior of men and women than has hitherto prevailed. This can only do good.

These beliefs of mine do not mean that I consider the Kinsey Reports to be perfect. I do not. Each of the two volumes thus far published suffers from certain faults, some of them serious. I have already dealt with the volume on the male in a preceding essay. In the present contribution I shall restrict my remarks to the volume on the female.

I greatly welcome *Sexual Behavior in the Human Female* because the most important finding in that book corroborates my own observations published in my book *The Natural Superiority of Women* (Macmillan, 1953; rev. ed., 1968). I refer to the finding by the Kinsey workers that women are far less easily aroused sexually by a whole host of external stimuli than men, and that they are much less preoccupied with sex than men. Kinsey's statistics explode the myth of female sexuality forever. And if ever there was a perfect example of myth, this is one, for as the Kinsey workers demonstrate, it is utterly false. Of the thirty-three psychosexual stimuli which arouse the male erotically, only three—movies, reading romantic literature, and being bitten—aroused as many or more females than males. There is, of course, great individual variation, but there can be no doubt about the sex differences as a whole.

The Kinsey workers have reversed the traditional belief, now shown to be false, that women are creatures of sex while men are in control of sex. The opposite is true. Most women have known this for generations, but they don't seem to have had much drive to say so. Simone de Beauvoir, in her book *The Second Sex*, points out that the female is not easily aroused. "Woman's erotic induction is not easy," she writes. "Man is impetuous, woman is only impatient." This is not really good enough. It is typical of much else in this distinguished book. Here the Kinsey facts are very much more impressive than the many pages of Simone de Beauvoir's animadversions on the comparative passiveness of the female.

In all cultures from the very beginning of time women have been at a disadvantage *vis-à-vis* the male. Men are physically stronger, and women are numerically more frequent. In 1969, for example, there are nearly 3.5 million more women than men. Where the disproportion between the sexes in status and number is so great, as it has been and still is, the female, in order to cope with the male, has been forced to resort to a large number of devices to make her sexually attractive—hence, the *seeming* preoccupation of the female with sex. As I point out in my book *The Natural Superiority of Women,* the behavior of women in our culture has largely been tailored in response to the behavior of males toward them. "Men have placed a high premium upon sexual attractiveness; the promised dividends are high, and women, therefore, concentrate on making themselves sexually attractive. But, we repeat, it is the men who are possessed by sex, not the women." By virtue of his statistics, Kinsey will enable men to see the truth and significance of these facts very much more cogently than I could. It may be hoped and expected that the feminine mood will less frequently be mistaken for disinterest or frigidity than it has been in the past.

If one asks the question: How does it come about that Kinsey's 5,940 women behave sexually the way they do? the answers offered are at the most superficial and unconvincing levels. Women behave as they do, Kinsey tells us, because they are forced into a compromise among innate biological drives, social restrictions and pressures, and psychological attitudes instilled by the social mores. I should think that this was a pretty obvious kind of statement, and as far as it goes it is true enough, but it can hardly be said to go below the surface, for though Kinsey sets out some of the details, the details insofar as the emotional development of his women is concerned scarcely begin to scratch the surface. Kinsey doesn't appear to be very interested in emotions. If he is, he gives little appearance of being so in this volume. The IBM machine doesn't seem to be equipped to handle emotions, and polling the ladies even with 600 questions somehow doesn't seem to yield any answers to the question: What makes these women tick sexually the way they do?

As an example of the manner in which the lack of interest in human emotions affects and coarsens the Kinsey workers' approach to their subject, analysis of the relation of religious devotion to sexual behavior may be cited as a case in point.

Altogether apart from the fact that devout Catholics and Orthodox Jews are inadequately represented in the sample, and that,
therefore, the sample is heavily weighted with women who are
likely to be sexually unconventional, the authors have failed
to deal with some very important variables with respect to the
religious background of their subjects.

The authors classified their women in three religious groups:
devout, moderately religious, and religiously inactive. As might
have been expected, they found: "In every one of the eleven
groups which are available for comparisons, definitely smaller
percentages of the religiously devout females and higher percentages of the religiously less devout or inactive females were
experiencing orgasm from any source prior to marriage."

So far, so good. But what I would really want to know, in
addition to the religious status of these women when they were
interviewed, is what kind of religious training they had received
in childhood, how religious they were in childhood, and for
what reasons and when they changed their religious status. I
believe that the analysis of such data would throw some light
upon the sexual behavior of these women, of a kind which we
have not been vouchsafed in the analysis provided by the Kinsey
team.

To illustrate what I mean, it is well known that when persons
who have been brought up in a religiously devout home give up
their religious beliefs they are likely to give up a great deal
along with them. Often they kick over the traces and, in reaction, indulge in highly unconventional behavior. Upon this
theme there are many variations. I should like to know something about them, particularly in relation to sexual behavior.
Neither the data nor the analysis of this interesting problem is
to be found in the Kinsey volume. But the Kinsey researchers
are not unaware of the problem, for they write: "It has been
possible to correlate the sexual data on these histories with the
current religious status of each subject, but it has not yet been
possible to make correlations with their earlier religious con-

nections. The earlier connections may have been the more significant in affecting the subsequent patterns of sexual behavior, but we will need a more extensive series than we yet have before we can undertake further analyses."

The indication is that the adequate information was not obtained for many of these women, and hence we shall have to wait until a sufficient number of women have been asked the proper questions. Possibly the Kinsey workers are about to make the momentous discovery that emotions exist.

The first volume of the Kinsey Reports was entitled *Sexual Behavior in the Human Male;* the second volume is entitled *Sexual Behavior in the Human Female.* Actually the first volume is concerned exclusively with the *American* male, and the second volume is concerned exclusively with the *American* female. The fact that neither volume is representative of the American population as a whole is acknowledged at the outset by the Kinsey team. "At its best," they write, "the present volume can pretend to report behavior which may be typical of no more than a portion, although probably not an inconsiderable portion, of the white females living within the boundaries of the United States. Neither the title of our first volume on the male, nor the title of this volume on the female, should be taken to imply that the authors are unaware of the diversity which exists in patterns of sexual behavior in other parts of the world."

This is a very necessary explanation, yet it does not eliminate the fact that the books are unsoundly titled. The titles imply either that only Americans are human or that what is true of Americans is true of all other human beings. A third implication is that no non-American has any sex life. We know that Dr. Kinsey meant to imply none of these things. These books deal with the sexual behavior of a very limited branch of humanity, namely, the American variety, and a small segment of that variety at that. With some qualifying phrase pointing out that each volume referred to the sexual life of a small and unrepresentative sample of the American population, the books should have been entitled *Sexual Behavior in the American Male* and *Sexual Behavior in the American Female*. It is difficult to understand why these important books, upon which so much care in almost every way has been lavished, were so inappropriately titled.

The title *Sexual Behavior in the Human Female* is doubly misleading, since the materials of the work are representative neither of the human female nor of the American female, but of a limited geographic sample of American women, more than 75 percent of whom went to college, and nearly 20 percent of whom had done graduate work!

Since Kinsey is himself not unaware of the dangers of generalization, it seems to me that he might have taken more care to avoid unjustified generalizations by beginning with the title of his book, by giving it a more accurate title which would properly prepare and orient the reader for the contents. By failing to do so, Kinsey must be held responsible for being the chief contributor to the misleading generalizations which will be made on the basis of what is, after all, the study of the sexual behavior of a small and selected sample of American women.

Were the readers of Kinsey's book to accept its findings for what they are worth, as a *statistical* accounting of the sexual behavior of a small sample of *atypical* American women, no great harm would be done. But this is not the manner in which a large number of readers are likely to take Kinsey's findings. That this is so is clear from the many newspaper and magazine articles which began to make their appearance before publication of the book, and which by now constitute a formidable library of the most diverse kinds of reporting and criticism. With very few exceptions these writings generalize Kinsey's findings for American women as a whole.

It cannot be too strongly emphasized that from every point of view such generalization is wholly unjustified. Kinsey's statements about "American women," or those of any other writer repeating or misrepeating Kinsey, are not true of American women as a whole, because Kinsey's sample is *not* representative of American women as a whole, but as he himself says, of only a small segment.

In spite of statistical and methodological inadequacies, *Sexual Behavior in the Human Female* is, in my considered judgment, one of the most important books on sexual behavior in human beings ever written. It would be so if it had only made clear, as the Kinsey researchers have, that females and males develop sexually at different rates and according to different patterns, that the male reaches his peak in his early teens and thereafter steadily declines, whereas the female matures sexually much more slowly and doesn't get to where the boy is in his early teens until her late teens or early twenties, and that while the male's sexual energies become increasingly dampened, the female maintains hers upon a more or less level plateau into her fifties or even sixties. Thus, in the earlier years the males generally want more coitus than their wives are ready to grant, while in the later years the females are ready for more coitus than the males are able to supply!

The authors are almost certainly right in suggesting that much marital unhappiness is brought about as a consequence of these misunderstandings which arise from the unrecognized disparities in the development of the sexes.

Contrary to prevailing popular ideas, the Kinsey workers have found that women of the higher educational levels are, significantly, sexually more responsive, as measured by frequency of orgasm, than those of the lower educational levels. This finding is contrary to an earlier, unpublished calculation made by the authors. It would have been interesting to learn whether there were any differences among the women who were educated in colleges for women as compared with coeducational institutions. I would surmise that the coeducational women did better than those who were educated in women's colleges.

That females are far less given to sexual perversities of every kind is another important finding. Homosexual contacts, for example, are much less frequent and there is much less promiscuity among females than among males. As the Kinsey workers point out, the widespread belief of the public at large and also of many clinicians that homosexual attachments occur more frequently among females than among males is very substantially demolished by their findings.

The correction of the many absurdities which circulate as knowledge concerning the dangers of premarital petting, masturbation, *und so weiter,* frequently reinforced by the *obiter dicta* of library scholars, constitutes yet another of the great services performed by the authors in the cause of clearer and healthier thinking and action.

The important discussions of the legal aspects of the various forms of sexual behavior will be of great service to those whose thinking needs to be clarified on this subject, as well as to those who may be legally interested. These discussions are eminently sound, far-reaching, and humane, and cause us to look forward with great interest to the volume or volumes which the authors will devote to this subject.

Above and beyond all, *Sexual Behavior in the Human Female* brings a much-needed wholesomeness to a subject much in need of it. The Kinsey workers thus continue in the tradition they set with the first volume. Humanity is greatly in their debt.

9. *The Sexual Superiority of Women*

There exists an old and widespread belief, in the societies of the Western world at least, that women are preoccupied with sex. This belief was most forcibly expressed in a famous European book published at the beginning of this century, *Sex and Character,* by a Viennese, Otto Weininger. Weininger, who was in his early twenties when the book was published, and therefore an authority on the subject, somewhat shrilly proclaimed: "Man possesses sex. Woman is possessed by it!"

Every man is, of course, an authority on sex, and every man, of course, knows that beauty parlors, hairdos, paints, pomades, powders, women's clothes, women's arts, and practically everything about women constitutes abundant testimony to their greater preoccupation with sex. Men shave, comb their hair, and wear drab clothes. They are interested in sex, of course, but their interest is as nothing compared with the interest of women—and by "interest" men usually mean a preoccupation with sex. So goes the current belief. I have done what I could to destroy that myth, for it is nothing less, in my book *The Natural Superiority of Women* (rev. ed., Macmillan, 1968). Kinsey and his co-workers, in their *Sexual Behavior in the Human Female,* for the first time in detail set out the facts which should forever explode the myth of "female preoccupation with sex" beyond possible reconstitution. In so doing, they demonstrated the sexual superiority of the female in almost every respect but that of sexual athleticism, a dubiously masculine trait upon which the male so weakly and overcompensatingly prides himself.

Since definitions are much more meaningful at the end of an inquiry than they can possibly be at the beginning of one, let us postpone our definition or analytic account of what we mean by "sexual superiority" until it has become so obvious to the reader in evaluating the facts for himself that the formal definition becomes doubly meaningful when he eventually comes upon it.

"Psychologic Factors in Sexual Response": Under this heading the Kinsey workers have reported:

> In general, males are more often conditioned by their sexual experience, and by a greater variety of associated factors, than females. While there is great individual variation in this respect among both females and males, there is considerable evidence that the sexual responses and behavior of the average male are, on the whole, more often determined by the male's previous experience, by his association with objects that were connected with his previous sexual experience, by his vicarious sharing of another individual's sexual experience, and by his sympathetic reactions to the sexual responses of other individuals. The average female is less often affected by such psychologic factors. It is highly significant to find that there are evidences of such differences between the females and males of infra-human mammalian species, as well as between human females and males.

Kinsey might have said not only "infra-human mammalian species" but almost the whole of the animal kingdom. It has long been known that in almost all sexual species of animals the female is likely to be the more quiescent and the male the more active creature. This idea was explicitly stated by Geddes and Thomson in their famous book *The Evolution of Sex:*

"It is generally true that the males are more active, energetic, eager, passionate, and variable; the females more passive, conservative, sluggish, and stable." [1]

Undoubtedly there is a profound phylogenetic basis for this difference between the sexes. Geddes and Thomson were the first to offer the hypothesis that the female organism is characterized by a predominance of constructive utilization of energy, by *anabolism* as compared with *catabolism,* or destructive utilization of energy. This hypothesis has been widely adopted. It is a useful and an interesting hypothesis, but actually it doesn't go far enough in explaining the differences between the sexes with reference to the end they are designed to serve. The end which the sexes are designed to serve is reproduction of the species. But reproduction of the species is not enough; the species must be maintained. It is here that the difference between the sexes most importantly expresses itself, for while it is the function of the male to produce fertilization, it is the function of the female to be fertilized and in the mammals to maintain the uterine-developing organism and see it through not only to successful birth but infancy and childhood. With comparatively few exceptions this is true of the whole animal kingdom. One may readily see, then, why the female is likely to be anabolic and the male catabolic. From the standpoint of survival the female is vastly more important biologically than the male, and it is therefore important that she be a conserver rather than a dissipator of energy. As Tinbergen has pointed out: "Since the female carries the eggs for some time, often even after fertilization, and since in so many species the female takes a larger share than the male in feeding and protecting the young, she is the more valuable part of the species' capital. Also, one male can often fertilize more than one female, an additional reason why individual males are biologically less valuable than females. It is therefore not surprising that the

[1] *The Evolution of Sex* (London & New York, 1889), p. 270.

female needs persuasion more than the male, and this may be the main reason why courtship is so often the concern of the male." [2]

The overall biological superiority of the female lies, then, in the fact that she is the more valuable part, as Tinbergen puts it, of the species' capital because she is the principal maintainer and protector of the species during their most precarious and important periods of development. In this fact is also to be found the explanation of the difference in sexual interest between female and male. When Kinsey records these differences in psychosexual response in as great detail as he does, he is probably quite right in seeing some significant connection between such differences in human beings and similar differences in "infra-human mammalian species."

Now, what are these psychologic factors in sexual response which Kinsey investigated? They were such factors as observing the opposite sex, nude figures, one's own sex, erotic fine art, genitalia, exhibitionism, movies, burlesque and floor shows, sexual activities, portrayals of sexual activities, animals in coitus, peeping and voyeurism, preferences for light or dark, fantasies concerning sex, sex dreams, diversion during coitus, stimulation by literary materials, erotic stories, writing and drawing, wall inscriptions, discussions of sex, and the like. Altogether 33 such factors were investigated, and it was only in respect of three items—movies, reading romantic literature, and being bitten—that as many males or more females than males seem to have been affected. In respect of 29 of the 33 items fewer females than males were affected.

While there can be little doubt that social conditioning plays a considerable role in influencing patterns of sexual response, and that the male in this respect seems to be much more conditionable than the female in our culture, there can be equally little doubt that there exists a profound biological difference

[2] N. Tinbergen, *Social Behavior in Animals* (New York: Wiley, 1953), p. 22.

between the sexes in this respect. The male seems to be in a chronic state of sexual irritation. The woman who, in a letter to Kinsey, described the race of males as "a herd of prancing, leering goats" was being rather generous. It is the male who is preoccupied with sex, and his preoccupation with sex in Western culture is at a very superficial level. The male of the Western world is the gadfly of sex; he'll mate with any woman he encounters. The female, on the other hand, is much less occupied with sex than the male. She is not in a chronic state of sexual irritation; she is not, as the male is, in a state of continuous rut. Sexual response in the female has to be aroused, and it cannot be aroused by superficial stimulation. Sex *means* more to the female than it does to the male, and except for the highly abnormal instance of prostitution, she will not mate with any male she encounters.

These differences seem to be biologically based, and from every point of view they confer superiority—biological, moral, social, and aesthetic—on the female. The fact that these differences are biologically based does not, however, mean that the male's behavior is either excusable or irremediable. It makes it, perhaps, a little more understandable. Certainly, in many parts of the civilized world many highly sexed men have managed not to become sexual gadflies and have exercised their claim to being called human by respecting themselves as much as they have other people—including women.

The promiscuous male is not determined by biology but largely produced by an inadequate education in the meaning of human relations. The biological drives require satisfaction, and they appear to have a much greater pressor effect and a lower excitation threshold than in the female. Society must learn to understand this and enable the male to regulate his drives in a more satisfactory manner than he has, for the most part, succeeded in achieving in our culture.

From an anthropological study published a few weeks after the appearance of the Kinsey Report we learn: "Throughout

Brazil the idea is commonly held that men do not wish to marry. Several people explained that a young man does not willingly take on the heavy responsibilities of a permanent union and renounce the pleasures of sexual adventure." [3] We are not surprised—with sufficient encouragement men would everywhere behave in much the same manner. The fact is, however, that from the point of view of biological and social health of a society such encouragement would have unfavorable results. Premarital sexual license is one thing, but the unwillingness to marry and become responsible for one's own family is quite another. It is here, too, that the pull of women to legalize illicit unions, to drag the unwilling male to the altar, has from the earliest times exercised a beneficial effect on human society.

Women have been aware of the waywardness of the errant male, doubtless from the earliest times, and for this reason they have been forced to resort to every possible device in order to make themselves attractive to the male and to maintain their attractiveness in order to secure the interest of this sexually preoccupied creature. Hence, the powders, the pomades, the paint, the pulchritude, and the equation in the male's mind (and in the minds of some women) of sex with love.

Unfortunately the female's much higher threshold of sexual excitability, the ease with which she is distracted even during intercourse from what is for the male the focus of all his attention, has already led many readers of the Kinsey Report to conclude that women are not very interested in sex. This is but one example of the dangerous and utterly erroneous kind of conclusion which will be drawn, as a result of Kinsey's own lack of clarity, from his report. By comparison with women, men are more superficially interested in sex and make up in quantitative activity what they fail to experience qualitatively. On the contrary, the female is more profoundly interested in sex, and the quality of her interest is very much more sensitively

[3] Charles Wagley, *Amazon Town* (New York: Macmillan, 1953), p. 169.

developed than that of the average male. Hence, the average male's crass sexual approaches to the female are unlikely to elicit her happiest responses.

It is, however, doubtful that with the most consistently perfect approaches the female would, on the average, ever respond as continuously as the male does to the appropriate psychosexual stimulation. The male can, as it were, turn the faucet of sex on at a moment's notice; it takes somewhat more than a moment in the average female.

For the female, sex is a human relationship; for the male, relationships with women tend to be in terms of sex. Sex without love is no more meaningful for most women than it is for most men. Even the professional prostitute has one kind of sex for her customers and another kind for her lover. Most men, however, in their approach to sex think in terms of *doing something to* a woman that gives them (the men) pleasure. These are not the words usually used; other less printable words are, and they convey the thought that the male satisfied himself on his quarry. No woman, with the exception of the prostitute, ever describes a sexual relationship with a man in such terms. Her relationship is *with* the man and not, as it were, in opposition to him.

The sexual attitudes of most males in the Western world toward the female are scarcely distinguishable from those of the female professional prostitute toward "the trick" or "John," that is, her male client. It is essentially an exploitative attitude in which the other is considered generally of very little worth.[4]

In general it may be said that men are sexual creatures, whereas women are reproductive creatures, and in the sex relationship, as in others, women tend to humanize men. Hence in all relationships, and especially in the sexual relationship, what women beyond all else want from men is an expression of involvement, caring, tenderness, and sensitiveness to her vulner-

4 James H. Bryan, "Occupational Ideologies and Individual Attitudes of Call Girls," *Social Problems*, Vol. 13, No. 4 (Spring, 1966), pp. 441–50.

ability, responses which she so seldom receives from the crasser male. In these attributes the female is, of course, vastly superior to the male.

It is an unfortunate fact that in the cultures of the Western world, and especially in its English-speaking segment, there exists a taboo on the expression of tenderness,[5] a taboo which is sedulously taught boys, the emphasis being on "toughness." Tenderness and gentleness are looked upon as behavior fit only for a "sissy." Our men have a great deal to learn about the nature of being human, and women have a great deal to teach them. Will they succeed? It is an open question. It would be greatly helpful if men began to understand the problem and commenced to cooperate with women.

By virtue of her natural reticences, a woman is naturally on the side of morality and the proprieties; in these respects, also, she is therefore naturally superior to the male. The female seems to come by these qualities naturally, although there can be small doubt that social influences play a considerable role in determining what she will consider moral and proper. The male will always, obviously, have a harder time behaving himself, but that he can learn to keep himself happily in check has fortunately been many times demonstrated. The proper education in human relations will enable the healthy-minded male to adjust to himself and to other human beings as he ought. It is time that we realized that the improvement he must make in the conduct of his sexual life will not be brought about through better "sex education" but through better education in human relations, for sex behavior is merely an aspect of human relations, of one's personal attitudes toward other human beings. It is possible that when the male of the future looks back on the history of his sex he will perceive that its failure was in the realm of human relations.

The male doesn't understand the female, and Kinsey's book

[5] See the admirable chapter on this subject in Ian Suttie's *The Origins of Love and Hate* (New York: Julian Press, 1952).

abundantly testifies to this. The female has always had a much better understanding of the male than the male has had of the female, and a fortunate thing, indeed, this has been for human society. Kinsey's *Sexual Behavior in the Human Female* has done much toward increasing the understanding of the sexes for each other. Meanwhile, the female's better understanding of the male is again a mark of her superiority.

Furthermore, Kinsey shows that the female never reaches an abrupt peak of sexuality, as does the male, but that she develops more slowly and steadily, and that while the male's sexual powers are waning hers are maintaining their steady level well into her fifties or sixties.

Whatever may eventually be held accountable for this difference the conclusion is obvious: In the duration of their sexual ardor women outlast men by a considerable margin. "There is little evidence" writes Kinsey, "of any aging in the sexual capacities of the female until late in her life."

It may now be apparent to the reader what we have meant by "sexual superiority" throughout this chapter. Perhaps a definition may now be acceptable on the basis of our findings. By sexual superiority we mean sexual behavior of a kind which confers survival benefits on all who participate in it, and which confers humanly creatively enlarging benefits upon all who come within the orbit of its influence. The female enjoys this sexual superiority by fiat, as it were, of nature, but there is absolutely no reason why the male cannot learn to adjust himself harmoniously to the female and acquire by "second nature" those controls with which the female has for the most part been endowed by nature. In this task the fundamental facts provided by Kinsey should be of the greatest assistance.

As Kinsey makes clear, many avoidable tragedies of marriage are directly traceable to the ignorance which prevails concerning the fundamental differences that exist in the development of the sexual drives of female and male. In early marriage the male desires more coitus than his wife is ready to respond to.

In later life she wants more than he is able to give, but she isn't nearly as concerned as the male is in the early years of marriage when he finds that his wife isn't as frequently responsive as he thinks she ought to be. With deeper understanding of the facts of life it will be possible for both women and men to adjust these differences in a mutually satisfactory manner. In marriage, as in all human relations, happiness is necessarily reciprocal and is found only in being given. Success in marriage depends not so much on finding the right person as on *being* the right person.

The biologically based differences between the sexes insofar as behavior is concerned do not need to be changed; what needs to be changed is our traditional way of dealing with them. In short, it is not human nature which should be changed, but human nurture. Here the sexes can cooperatively work together to find a better way of living together than has thus far been achieved.

10. *Sex Made to Order*

Many times more bold than those who are so venturesome as to attempt to predict sex are the people who have tried through the ages to make sex to their own specifications. Men have been trying to do this for thousands of years. Their failure must have been obvious in at least 50 percent of cases. Yet seemingly they have never been discouraged.

One of the oldest formulas is given in the *Susrutas Ayur-Vedas* of the ancient Hindus, which dates back to the sixth century B.C. The husband who desires a boy is instructed to have intercourse with his wife on the fourth, sixth, tenth, and twelfth night after menstruation, each time following consoling prayers. If he wants a daughter, he joins his wife on the fifth, seventh, ninth, and eleventh nights.

In the *Tractate Niddah* of the Hebrew Talmud, the statement is made that if the woman takes part more passionately than the man, then a boy will be conceived; if the man takes part more passionately than the woman, then it will be a girl.

Other methods were suggested by the right-left theory. That theory held that a boy was produced in the "right chamber" of the womb, a girl in the "left chamber." (Actually the womb is not divided into chambers—except in some other animals.) The German writer Eucharius Roesslin advised that if a woman wanted a boy, she was to "lean to the right side immediately after the act." Roesslin wrote that in 1513. The belief is still held by some today. Some stock breeders have their cows "served" while standing on the side of a hill. If a bull calf or a stallion is wanted, the female is placed with her right flank sloping downhill; if vice versa, vice versa.

Some theorists rang a change on the right-left theory and argued that sex was determined solely by the male: if the sperm came from the right testicle, a boy was the result; if from the left testicle, a girl. Anaxagoras propounded this idea in the fifth century B.C., and like every other high-sounding error, it has never died, despite science, despite education. François Mauriceau, seventeenth-century Parisian physician, tried to refute this theory by recounting the case of an Italian he knew who had only one testicle, the left. The man's wife gave birth to both a boy and a girl, Mauriceau pointed out. "Nor," he added, "needed he suspect his wife had the assistance of any other in the business, as it very often happens in this country."

Despite Mauriceau, the theory was revived in 1786 by one J. Hencke. And a hundred years after that, the famous British medical journal *The Lancet* printed a letter stating that "from many inquiries I have made among my married friends, I have no hesitation in saying that when men are in the habit of sleeping on the right side of their wives, they beget male children, and when on the left—females." It is possible that this letter was a hoax, but *The Lancet* considered it seriously enough to ask the correspondent sharply, "How is the variation in sex in the same family to be accounted for?"

But the right-left theory went merrily on. In 1917 a 200-page book reviving it was published by a physician, E. Rumley Dawson, member of the Council of the Obstetrical Society of London and Fellow of the Royal Society of Medicine. He said he had a new slant. It wasn't the right or left testicle or the right and left side of the womb that determined sex: it was the right and left ovary, and so on. Cells from the right ovary produce boys; from the left ovary, girls. From here on, sex determination is easy. First the husband and wife have to have a child. If it's a girl, they know the cell came from the left side. Next month it will come from the right side. Thus, they keep track of menstruations, and at any month they know whether a male or female cell is coming up. Thus they can pick the sex they want.

Dawson claimed to have predicted the sex of the last three children of the Empress of Russia by this method.

Unfortunately for Dawson, a paper was published just a year later demolishing his theory. The paper was based on 75 Caesarian operations at Johns Hopkins Hospital. During this operation it is possible to examine the ovaries for the *corpus luteum,* the yellowish scar caused by the escape of the egg cell, and thus determine from which side the fertilized egg had come. Murray found, in the 75 cases studied, that male and female children came in approximately equal numbers from both ovaries.

Another long-held popular theory is that the time of conception determines the sex. In the *Tractate Berakoth* of the Hebrew Talmud one of the sages is quoted as saying, "He who sets his bed between midnight and midday gets a child of male sex." Two German savants, C. Duesing and V. Goehlert, got together statistics purporting to prove that girls are produced mostly in spring and summer, boys in autumn and winter.

T. E. Reed, in *Sex, Its Origin and Determination,* published in 1913, gave all the credit to the tides. Designating the six hours of rising tide as the "positive phase," and the six hours of ebbing tide the "negative phase," he says: "Coitus taking place at or near the middle of the positive phase ... a male is the result; while at or near the middle of the negative or passive phase, a female is conceived."

What about coitus that takes place midway—when the tide is neither coming in nor going out? Very unreliable, Reed says. You don't know what you'll get.

Many sex savants claimed to have discovered significance in the date of conception as compared with the date of menstruation. Hippocrates, who contributed a great many valuable ideas, opined that a man who wanted a son should have relations with his wife immediately after menstruation. That theory knocked around for 2,500 years or so, and then, in 1886, C. Fuerst, a German investigator, reported that a study of 193 pregnancies showed that they resulted in most cases in boys when the conception had taken place four days after the end of menstruation. More recently, P. W. Siegel presented rather more "convincing" data, based on 115 German women who gave birth during World War I. In each case the father was a soldier with only a short furlough, so the date of conception could be figured rather closely. Siegel says he found that if conception took place during the first nine days following the start of menstruation, 86 percent of the children born were boys. If conception took place from the fifteenth to the twenty-third day, 84 percent were females.

The above two reports look quite impressive, until one notices the small number of cases involved—193 in the first study, 115 in the second. Drawing conclusions from too few cases is the most fruitful source of error. Even scientists are sometimes the victim of this failing.

But this has not exhausted the list of theories—not by a long way. In 1717 Caspar Nigrino advised that a man who wanted a son should limit his unions with his wife to no more than three or four times a month. Such restraint, he declared, causes the "seed" to become "thicker, more matured and more filled with spirits"—and hence more likely to produce a male.

One scientist claimed to have discovered that men younger than thirty and those older than forty-five had sons more often than men thirty-one to forty-four. Others found that boys happened more often when the husband was considerably older than the wife than when the ages were close together. Still others have pointed to weather and climate. But Scheinfeld, who studied the birth records of Northern and Southern states, found no difference in the sex ratios. Another popular scientific speculation is that underfeeding produces more males. One scientist, in a study of 5,000 cases, found that among the poor there were 115 boys to every 100 girls, whereas among the well-to-do the ratio was only 104 boys to 100 girls. The noted German obstetrician Hermann Ploss actually claimed to have demonstrated a parallelism between the rise and fall of food prices and the fluctuations of the male-female ratio.

The trouble with all these studies has been the same defect—conclusions based on too few cases. By working with a few cases, one can "prove" almost anything. One can expect almost any day to hear somebody "prove" the relationship between longer (or shorter) women's dresses and the sex of their offspring.

One common belief, in which fact has become entangled with myth, is that there is a great increase in male births during or following a long war. Several investigators have claimed to have observed this phenomenon, but still others have failed to find any evidences of it. At the present time the status of this belief is in the "suspense account." It is not known whether it is true or false. When this thesis is stated with authority, the awed superstitious mind has it as proof of the workings of compassionate Nature, making up for the numbers of males killed. Sober scientists, while not claiming to be able to offer a satisfactory explanation, do advance the following suggestions: (1) in wartime, there is a tendency for younger persons to marry, and younger mothers give birth to a higher percentage of males; and (2) the separation of husbands and wives gives the latter a vacation from childbearing, leaving them stronger for future childbearing, with a consequent greater likelihood of male births.

To understand these explanations, it may help the reader to review briefly present-day knowledge about how sex is determined—the real story, separate from myth and magic. The ejaculate that comes from the male contains two kinds of sperm —several hundred million sperm—all of one or two types, one called the X type, the other the Y type. These sperm are produced in equal numbers. They are ejaculated into the female vagina and commence to swim through the female secretions up into the womb and then into one of the Fallopian tubes or egg ducts, where an egg cell (the ovum) is freshly passing toward the womb. If a Y sperm gets to the egg first and penetrates it, the resulting union will be a male; if an X sperm wins the race, the result will be a female. It is that, and that alone, that determines sex of offspring.

Since there are equal numbers of X and Y sperms, one might assume that in the long run equal numbers of boys and girls would be born. But we have seen in Chapter 8 that this is not the case. Apparently the Y sperm—the male-producing sperm—is sturdier or speedier or has some other selective advantage over the X sperm. So more male embryos are conceived—a ratio estimated at about 120 to 170 males to 100 females. But once the male embryo is conceived, life begins to bear down on it. It has a much greater tendency to be aborted or to be stillborn than the female. By the time nine months are completed, the ratio has dropped to 105 males to 100 females.

Now we can perceive why statistics show that younger mothers and mothers whose childbearing is spaced out give birth to more boys. In both cases, the mother is stronger than the average, in a better physical state, and thus in a better condition to bring to full term those male embryos that are conceived. In other words, the prenatal male death rate is reduced. Thus, the common belief that more male babies are produced following wars is really wrong-end reasoning from the fact that fewer male embryos die. There is a large increase in the number of babies born to young mothers, and therefore a significant increase in the number of *surviving* male babies.

A belief one encounters quite often is that stronger sexuality on the part of the man procures boys, whereas stronger feelings in the mother produce girls. Unfortunately, this belief runs counter to another, equally widespread, that a father who produces girls exclusively is lacking in virility. In this way popular superstitions cancel each other out. However, in 1951 Dr. Marianne Bernstein, on the basis of a statistical study, cited evidence to show that more aggressive men tend to have more male offspring than less aggressive ones. But much independent study will have to be carried out before this finding can be accepted. Independent verification is the scientific way.

Students of folklore have picked up all sorts of beliefs among Europeans and European immigrants into the United States about methods for predetermining sex. In all cases the suggested method is aimed at producing a male. Thus, in the Tyrol of Italy the husband who wants to beget a boy wears boots during the sexual act. If that doesn't work, he can try smearing his sexual organ with hare's blood. In some parts of Germany the farmers believe strongly in the value of intercourse during rainstorms. In other places reliance is placed on intercourse during the waxing moon. (The waning moon supposedly produces girls.) In southern France the tradition is for Papa to wear his hat during the crucial moment if he wants a boy. In some sections of Poland man and wife put on their Sunday clothes for the male-begetting act.

Perhaps the most spectacular pronunciamento concerning determination of sex came from Dr. F. Unterberger of Königsberg, Germany, in 1932. He claimed to have discovered that maleness was associated with alkalinity and femaleness with acidity. Thus, all one had to do to produce males was to give the woman a douche of one percent solution of bicarbonate of soda immediately before coitus. This would produce an environment very favorable for the Y type of sperm. If female offspring were desired, one used a one percent solution of lactic acid, which would produce an environment discouraging to the Y sperm and favorable to the X, or female-producing, sperm.

Unterberger claimed that the bicarbonate of soda method resulted in male births for 74 women—all of whom had previously given birth to from one to four girls. His theory was that the alkaline medium stimulates the Y sperm to swim more rapidly and thus reach the ovum faster than the X sperm.

The New York *Daily News,* which has always considered sex its specialty, subsidized animal experiments to test Unterberger's theory—with rather dismal results. Independent studies carried out at various universities failed to support Unterberger's claims. But despite these various failures, it seems likely that the time will come when science will develop a method of predetermining sex. Some chemical may be found which, if injected into the female, will aid one type of sperm cell and hinder or destroy the other. Another possible method which has been suggested is the collection of sperm from the male and the separation of X sperm from Y sperm by electrical or chemical action, or by centrifuging them—much in the way cream is separated from milk. The assumption here is that the X sperm is heavier than the Y sperm. Then one type will be discarded, and the other—depending on the sex desired—will be injected into the female uterus.

However, whether this will lead to greater happiness or unhappiness is anybody's guess. One thing we *can* reasonably predict is that if such a method were developed, we would soon hear of divorces based on the charge that the other spouse wanted boys instead of girls or vice versa.

11. *What Will You Have—Boy or Girl?*

Never, since it was first discovered that children were born with different sexes, have people been willing patiently to wait nine months to find out what they were getting. Since earliest recorded times, they have concocted various sorts of magic to foretell sex or have gone to sages who claimed they could do it. And in every age and land, up to the present day, there has been no lack of sages with this special gift.

The reason for this intense curiosity was, in most cases, no mere neurotic impatience. The birth of a boy carried large premiums of happiness; a girl, the reverse. A boy meant another warrior, another hunter in the family. A boy would need no dowry in marriage. A boy could perform the proper rites upon the parents' death. The Chinese, for example, believe that unless the family has a son to carry out the necessary rituals, the deceased father will hunger and thirst perpetually in the other world. Thus, some Chinese families give to an only daughter such names as Call a Boy or Beckoning for Your Brother. In some parts of Switzerland a relative of the mother announces the birth by wearing a corsage if the baby is a girl—a corsage plus bouquet if the baby is a boy. Among European royalty there used to be a 101-gun salute for the birth of a prince, but only 35 guns for a princess. The more reserved British have more equably reduced this to 21 guns for the birth of a royal heir and 20 for a princess.

Among the Montenegrins the mother of several daughters and no sons was expected to summon seven orthodox priests to chase the evil spirits from her home with holy oil. Where infanticide has been practiced, it has almost always been female infanticide. Mohammed had to denounce the Arabs of his time for the practice of burying female infants. Destruction of female offspring has been reported in modern times in China, New Caledonia, New Guinea, and Greenland.

In America, the preference for boys is still widespread, even though the economic and social bases for it have largely disappeared. A girl can in many cases bring as much income into the family as a boy, and she is usually more loyal and dependable in maintaining the family ties. Traditions, however, never die easily, and the preponderant vote still is for boys.

Equally long-lived is the belief that the sex can be foretold. Dr. Alan Guttmacher questioned pregnant women in the wards of Johns Hopkins Hospital and found a large number who were sure they could tell the sex they had under their belts. He tells the varied answers he got:

If the baby kicks on the right side, it will be a boy; if it kicks on the left, it will be a girl.

If the pregnancy is carried "high," it will be a boy; if it is carried "low," it will be a girl.

If the patient loses her hair during pregnancy, it will be a girl; if the hair grows thick and long, it will be a boy.

If the baby moves actively in the uterus, it will be a boy.

If the abdomen is round, it will be a boy; if it sticks out in a point, it will be a girl.

If the patient develops a preference for sweet foods, it will be a girl; if she prefers sour foods, it will be a boy.

If the patient is nauseated during pregnancy, a boy can be expected. As one prospective mother said, "Boys always make me sicker."

Many of these beliefs can be traced, without change, straight back to the Greek philosophers of 2,500 years ago. Parmenides of Elea, who lived in the fifth century B.C., started this train of errors when he examined the entrails of cows, found that the womb had a left and right chamber, and mistakenly assumed that human females are similarly constructed. He decided that males must be produced in the right chamber, females in the left—since males are stronger and more desirable in every way, and hence could be associated only with the right, or stronger, side of the body.

Variations of this theory have been repeated in all the centuries since. Among the Hindus, the Romans, and the Hebrews it was commonly believed that if the mother's abdomen was bigger on the right side, one could be certain of a boy. Mano-ello, a Jewish physician of fourteenth-century Rome, skipped the abdomen and said you could tell by the nostrils: if the woman's right nostril bled, a boy was sure. Abulcasis, the great Muslim surgeon of the tenth century, averred that the birth of a female was portended by retraction of the left nipple. Avicenna, the Mohammedan physician of the eleventh century, came out with a whole catalog of signs. A woman bearing a male child, he said, had a stronger pulse in her right wrist than in her left; she always started walking with her right foot; she reached for things with her right hand; her right eye was more sparkling than her left.

Note how all these beliefs associate the male with the right side—the stronger, luckier, sounder side. Other beliefs claim a happier, healthier appearance on the part of a woman bearing a son—as if Nature were tickled pink at the event. Hippocrates averred that a male sign was a good complexion in a pregnant woman. Rhazes, the Arab physician, believed the same of bright red nipples. Jacques Guillemeau, renowned French physician, wrote in 1609 that a woman bearing a daughter has a pale face and a "melancholy eye." A similar belief is reported today among Turkish midwives.

One of the commonest beliefs today is that a boy does more

kicking in the womb. This is another one of the chestnuts perpetrated by Hippocrates 2,500 years ago. He stated categorically that a male child starts moving three months after conception, the girl at four months. Curiously, in modern Tunisia, the belief in the three-month schedule still exists, although the time for the girl to start kicking has been moved up to five months.

The fact is that the bones of the female start hardening (ossification) one to two months earlier than those of the male; and hence if either one kicks first, it ought to be the girl. However, the fact of earlier ossification of the bones in the female is not to be recommended as a formula for amateur sex prognosticators.

In the 1860's a great deal of prominence was given to the theory that the heart rate of the male and female fetuses differed and thus presented a sure method of predicting sex. Frankenhauser stated that a rate of 124 beats or fewer a minute indicated a boy; 144 or more, a girl. This sounded convincing, just like a great many other "scientific" reports. And like a lot of other "scientific" reports, further checks by others failed to corroborate the difference in heartbeat and thus the conclusions.

About thirty years ago several German scientists went to work on the theory that blood from a woman should contain substances which would digest testicular tissue obtained from animals. Their experiments led to a report in 1926, by R. Dryoff, that he had accurately predicted sex in this way in 72 out of 98 cases. To put it another way, he failed in 26 cases, which should have discouraged the mothers asked to participate.

In November, 1932, J. H. Dorn and E. I. Sugarman reported successful prediction in 80 out of 85 cases with an original method. They injected young male rabbits with urine from pregnant women. If the fetus was female, they said, the testicles of the rabbits showed precocious growth changes within forty-eight hours; if the fetus was male, there was no change. However, attempts made at Woman's Hospital, New York, to confirm this test were unsuccessful.

A hormonal test was reported in October, 1951, by Dr. William Gustav Rapp, biochemist of Chicago's Loyola University. Dr. Rapp was originally interested in finding whether any secretions in addition to urine showed evidence of pregnancy. He tried, among other things, saliva, and found that when the test was positive a boy was born, when the test was negative a girl was born. Rapp's hypothesis is that the male fetus releases male hormones into the mother's system in sufficient quantity to be measurable in the saliva.

Dr. Rapp tested 400 women who were five to six months pregnant. His predictions proved accurate in 92 percent of cases. Unfortunately, other investigators do not appear to have had a similar success with this test.

It was not until 1949, with the discovery by Dr. Murray L. Barr of the University of Western Ontario that from the eighteenth day of the development any cell of an organism destined to be a female could be distinguished from any cell destined to be a male, that a practicable method of determining the sex of a child before birth became possible. The method is by an operation, not without its hazards, known as para-abdominal amniocentesis. This operation consists of introducing a needle through the mother's abdomen into the amniotic sac and withdrawing some of its fluid content. The fluid is likely to contain some of the cells shed by the fetus. If these cells show a small dark body at the periphery of the nuclear membrane, the child is a female. If the Barr body is absent, it is a male. The Barr, or chromatin, body is now known to be a condensed X chromosome, always present in the female and always absent in the male. Hence, it is possible to determine with certainty what the sex of the child will be.

While this operation has its uses in certain clinical cases, it is not recommended as a general procedure. A method of sex determination which is not attended with some risk both to the mother and fetus remains therefore to be developed. There is no doubt that someday it will be found.

12. *Virginity*

From the standpoint of biology and physiology, the part of the female sexual organs that is of least significance is the hymen, or maidenhead. From the standpoint of popular tradition, it is the most significant. It is synonymous with purity, with virginity. A torn hymen before marriage is proof of immorality. The tearing of the hymen changes a woman drastically. Getting married without being intact in this region means depriving the husband of the dearest delight in man's experience.

Examples of such beliefs can be found in the oldest recorded literatures. They are current all over the world. Yet every one of them is false.

Just what is this object which has been the source of so much controversy, misery, ritual, poetry, comedy?

Anatomically the hymen is a fold of mucous membrane partially closing the entrance to the vagina. It usually has a half-moon shape—about the size of a dime. It is usually torn during the first sexual intercourse; usually with bleeding and pain mixed with pleasure. It gradually is worn away during subsequent intercourse until nothing is left but a few tiny ridges where it was attached to the entrance rim.

But this description does not fit every case. What the ancients did not know—what few persons outside the medical profession know even today—is that the hymen is as variable in shape, in size, and in consistency as any other part of the body. Just as a woman may have a small nose or thick lips, so she may have a small or large hymeneal membrane. It can be thin or thick; stiff or flexible; sturdy or easily torn. It can be so rudimentary that only a trained gynecologist can detect its presence. It is subject to accidental tears in many ways—by strenuous gymnastics, horseback or even bicycle riding, a violent fall with legs spread apart.

What happens, then, to the male's stern dictum that a woman without an intact hymen is not a virgin? How does he know?

He is just as liable to error when he asserts the reverse proposition—that a woman with an intact hymen *is* a virgin. For sometimes the membrane is very elastic and does not tear even after repeated sexual experiences. Some investigators have reported cases of intact hymens in prostitutes. And there are even cases on medical record of intact hymens after childbirth!

Then again, a woman whose hymen has been torn by premarital intercourse can, if she wishes, have it repaired by surgery. That is an old bit of women's lore. The Persians have known for centuries how to restore virginity with a few stitches. The method was well known in sixteenth-century Spain; it was alluded to by Cervantes in the story "La Tia Fingida," in which a woman adept at this art says, "There is nothing on this earth to be compared with needle and flesh-colored twisted silk."

In view of the foregoing, one wonders at the hardihood of some medical examiners who categorically state in courts of law that a woman is or is not a virgin.

One thing most men are certain about, whatever their attitudes or beliefs about virginity, is that a sure sign of a virgin is copious bleeding on her wedding night. We find this belief embalmed in Deuteronomy 22:13–17, in which it is said that if a man takes a dislike to his bride and tries to defame her by charging she came to him already deflowered, her parents are to take the cloth (presumably the bedsheet) bearing the "tokens of the damsel's virginity" and show it to the city's elders in refutation. It was customary among the Copts of Egypt for a matron or even the bridegroom himself to examine the bride digitally before the marriage, in the presence of witnesses, to see whether blood could be drawn. In some parts of Russia the bridal nightgown and sheets were examined after the consummation of the marriage, and if satisfactorily stained, they were proudly exhibited by her family amid general rejoicing. Among the Esthonians, it used to be customary for the bride to send the bloody tokens as a gift to her mother-in-law. Among some Chinese groups, if "the luck-bringing red rose" does not appear at the consummation of the marriage, the wedding decorations are taken down, the guests hurriedly depart, and the disgraced husband may send his wife back to her mother.

The fact which was apparently unknown to the ancient Hebrews, the Copts, the Russians, the Esthonians, the Chinese— and many Americans—is that bleeding *usually* occurs at the first intercourse, but *not always*. If the hymen is very slight in size or very distensible, bleeding will not occur.

It is appalling to think of the unhappiness which has been caused through the centuries by ignorance of this simple fact. It is even more appalling to consider how widespread ignorance of this subject still is in this age of enlightenment.

In view of all the importance attributed to virginity in religion, folklore, and literature, one might assume that there is something biologically right about it, something inherent to make it universally valued. But that is not so, as a glance into anthropology books will show. Among many South Sea Islanders and many African tribes, there is a complete indifference to virginity. In fact, as Bronislaw Malinowski has stated, "Prenuptial license, that is, the liberty of free intercourse given to unmarried youths and girls, is by far the most prevalent form of chartered freedom, as well as the most important." Among the Tenggerese of Java, the men frequently prefer to marry widows rather than young women. Among the Votiaks, a Finno-Ugrian tribe, virginity in an adult unmarried woman is considered a disgrace, a proof that the woman has been unable to attract any man. Some peoples have considered it proper for the bride to be deflowered not by her husband but by some political or religious leader. Thus, among the Balantes of Senegambia, the tribal chieftain had the responsibility for deflowering all brides, a service for which he received rich gifts. A similar custom has been reported for some parts of India.

The slight concern of the ancient Romans in the matter of virginity is perhaps indicated by the fact that the first detailed Roman medical treatise on the female sexual organs, written by Soranus of Ephesus about A.D. 100, makes no mention of the hymen.

The most amazing of all the beliefs regarding virginity is that the woman who has lost her maidenhood prior to marriage robs her husband of some exquisite and unmatchable delight. With all the billions of marriages that have occurred since the start of recorded history, this myth should have been demolished centuries ago. Yet it seems to be almost universally believed by young bachelors, and even many married men think that their failure to experience something heavenly during the defloration process was due to some failing on their own part or on their bride's. Their disappointment and shame would naturally cause them to keep their experience to themselves, which probably accounts for the continuation of the myth among the unmarried.

The fact is that the hymen may be a troublesome, and sometimes unconquerable, obstruction to the male; and its tearing a source of pain to the woman. The pain is usually so slight as to be scarcely noticeable; sometimes, however, it may be quite appreciable. Instead of being a source of some rare delight, the hymen has often robbed the nuptial experience of its grace and carefree charm. Sometimes, if the groom is abrupt in his approach, the ensuing pain is enough to give the bride a lasting aversion toward all sexual relations.

Physicians have encountered so many cases of frigidity caused by the pain and shock attending the tearing, or unsuccessful tearing, of the hymen that many of them advise young women to have the membrane artificially stretched or cut a week or two before marriage. That means, of course, that the groom will take to his arms a woman who anatomically is not a "virgin," but no case has been reported yet in which a groom complained about it.

That defloration is an unpleasantly painful process is, in fact, a myth based on the reality that in some cases it has proven so. In almost all these cases a knowledge of the technique of sex would have avoided the pain inflicted on the woman by the clumsy male. The actual pain induced by the tearing of the hymen is normally very slight, and when two ordinarily sensitive people are involved, is completely obscured in the woman by the climactic pleasure of intercourse. The anticipatory fears which have been established on the basis of this myth are extremely unfortunate in that they induce a frame of mind in the anxious bride not unlike that of a lamb being led to the slaughter. The effects of such an attitude of mind may be very serious in more ways than one.

In some women this belief takes so neurotic a form that they believe the defloration to be equivalent to being "torn apart." Such women often decline to involve themselves with any man and remain unmarried.

It is recorded that one young Englishwoman, who consulted her mother on the subject the night before her marriage, received from her this piece of heroic advice: "Close your eyes, my dear, and think of the British Empire!"

Artificial defloration is considered a bold ultramodern departure in medical practice, but investigation shows it to have been practiced for centuries by nonliterate peoples. Among the Sakalava of West Madagascar the young women tear the hymen themselves before marriage. In some parts of India the girl's hymen is cut open by her mother during a nocturnal festival. Among some of the Australian aborigines this procedure is performed by the older men of the community on every girl as soon as she enters adolescence. In ancient Rome the bride performed the operation on herself, upon reaching adolescence, by close contact with the statue of the god Mantunus.

Virginity in the male is no longer as highly prized as it once was in our society; nevertheless the belief is still widespread that a girl loses something valuable if her bridegroom is not a virgin. The general opinion of informed persons would be very much to the contrary. The merits, or nonmerits, of virginity in the male are not here being argued. What is being presented are the facts, and the facts strongly indicate that one would no more want an inexperienced person in the marriage relationship than one would want such a person in any other relationship. Experience adds to the appreciation of the loved one and promotes the happiness of both. Terman, in 1938, in his book *Psychological Factors in Premarital Happiness*, wrote that in contrast to the slow tempo of many changes in our society, the trend toward premarital sex experience "is proceeding with extraordinary rapidity." Terman and his associates found that women born before 1890 were in 86.5 percent of cases virgins at marriage, while 50.6 percent of men were, whereas women born after 1910 were virgins at marriage in only 31.7 percent of cases, and only 13.6 percent of men were. *"If,"* remarked Terman, *"the drop should continue at the average rate shown for those born since 1890* virginity at marriage will be close to the vanishing point for males born after 1930 and for females born after 1940."* Both 1930 and 1940 are now some way behind us, and while it would obviously not be true to say that the virginal male or female at marriage no longer exists, their increasing rarity at once solves many of the problems we would here otherwise have to consider with respect to the practically nonexistent virginal male. As Terman conclusively showed, premarital intercourse does not lead to any reduction in the chances of marital happiness.

13. *Menstruation*

Anything so spectacular as a monthly discharge of blood is bound to evoke speculation, myth, and rumor. Many women never quite seem to recover from their first shock at this event; and many men, too, seem to find a curious fascination in it, for they are even more prolific in spreading myths about it than women are.

While the taboo placed upon menstruating women is not universal, it is widespread among the peoples of the earth and is apparently of great antiquity.

In general, wherever menstrual taboos exist, the female is considered to be unclean during the menstrual period. All these prohibitions probably have a similar origin: the fear of blood, especially menstrual blood which is commonly regarded as containing "evil humors." Furthermore, blood is naturally associated with injury and death, and on both counts, therefore, one is safer if one stays away from it. The next logical step would be to dignify such dread by institutionalizing it, by creating laws requiring the avoidance of any contact, direct or indirect, with women in so dangerous a state.

The prohibition on sexual intercourse during the menstrual period has come down to us with practically its original vigor, so that today there are many husbands and wives who consider it perfectly natural to abstain from each other during the menstrual period.

Actually it is anything but perfectly natural, and many students of sex have found that there is no harm in sexual relations during menstruation. In that most deservedly popular of all books on the subject, Dr. Theodor Van de Velde's *Ideal Marriage*, which has been a best seller since its original appearance in 1926, the learned author states that *"moderate* and *mutually desired* sexual intercourse between *healthy* partners during menstruation is quite unobjectionable" (the italics are his). He points out, however, that if there is any latent infection in the woman, it has a tendency to flare up during menstruation.

The taboo against intercourse during menstruation led naturally to another myth—that women have no sexual desire during menstruation. It has always pleased man to think that his woman cannot have any desire unconnected with his. This myth has taken a long time adying, because it is only in recent years that science has become uninhibited enough to investigate such matters.

Dr. G. V. Hamilton questioned 100 mature, well-educated women as to the ups and downs of their sexual ardor. Eleven reported greatest desire during menstruation. Katherine Davis, in her study *The Periodicity of Sex Desire*, also reported some women who listed the menstrual period as their high point. The percentage was small, but it may well be that it is not greater because the strong taboo against it depresses feelings which might otherwise flourish.

Masters and Johnson in their pioneer volume, *Human Sexual Response*, state, "Frequently it has been presumed that coital activity during menstruation will lead to acute physical distress on the woman's part. During the past ten years no clinical evidence to support this concept has been established. In short, from a purely physiological point of view, there is no contraindication to coition or automanipulation during menstruation." [1]

1 *Human Sexual Response* (Boston: Little, Brown, 1966), pp. 124–26.

Indeed, Masters and Johnson found that most women in their series of 331 were interested in and desired sexual activity during their menstrual periods. Only 33 of these women objected to sexual intercourse during menstruation on religious or aesthetic grounds.

But men are not the only mythmakers; women also are responsible for many of the misconceptions about menstruation. For example, many women will swear that dishes break, cups fall, and the cooking goes wrong when they are menstruating. Havelock Ellis tells about a lady violinist who claimed she could never play a concert during her period because the violin strings always broke. Women may blame these happenings on mysterious emanations from their bodies; but the true explanation is probably much simpler. The bodily changes during menstruation sometimes cause nervous upsets in high-strung women; and it is not hard to see why a woman in such a state is likely to knock over a cup or mix her recipes or wind a violin string too tightly.

Dr. M. Wickham has shown that women in the British Army services have a lower intelligence score during menstruation. And Dr. Katharina Dalton has found that girls taking advanced or ordinary level examinations during either the premenstrual or the menstrual period have a lower pass rate, lower distinction rate, and lower average mark than those taking these examinations in the intermenstrual or nonmenstrual period. These lower rates were the more markedly affected the longer the menstrual period lasted. In 42 percent of 91 girls whose normal menstruation pattern was known, the stress of ordinary examinations produced an alteration in their menstrual cycle. This resulted in more girls menstruating during examination week than would have been expected from their normal pattern. The tendency was for the cycle to be lengthened rather than shortened, but some girls experienced a temporary amenorrhea, that is, cessation of menstruation altogether.

Dr. Dalton's findings revealed that a girl suffers an average handicap of 5 percent when taking examinations in the paramenstrual period, that is, the premenstrual and menstrual periods. Such findings suggest that females should not be required to take examinations during the paramenstrual period. Dr. Dalton suggests that a separation of eight or more days between examinations would ensure that no candidate is wholly within the paramenstrual period, and thus is not suffering from its effects. Interestingly enough, Dr. Dalton's findings apparently represent the first statistical confirmation of the effect of emotional stress in altering the normal menstrual pattern.[2]

Dr. Dalton has also shown that there is a marked tendency among women who have committed crimes to have done so during the menstrual period. She interviewed a large number of women below the age of fifty-five and found that almost half the women had committed their crimes during menstruation or the premenstruum, 63 percent committing their crimes during the premenstruum.[3]

Indeed, every kind of female psychological disturbance has been recorded as in some way associated with the menstrual cycle. This should not be in the least surprising, since the hormonal changes occurring during the premenstruum and menstruation are experimentally well known to be capable of causing substantial changes in behavior and also of affecting every organ system.[4]

The fact is menstrual blood *is* different from ordinary blood, since it contains various substances not present in the latter during the nonmenstrual period. These substances appear to be principally long-chain fatty acids. When injected into guinea pigs, extracts of menstrual fluids cause contractions of the uterus

2 K. Dalton, "Menstruation and Examinations," *Lancet*, Vol. 2 (1968), pp. 1386–88.

3 K. Dalton, "Menstruation and Crime," *British Medical Journal*, Vol. 2 (1961), p. 1752.

4 F. A. Beach, *Hormones and Behavior* (New York: Hoeber, 1948); S. C. Freed and W. S. Kroger, "Psychologic Manifestations of the Menstrual Cycle," *Psychosomatic Medicine*, Vol. 12 (1950), pp. 229–35.

in these animals. It is now believed that it is these substances which are responsible for the contractions of the uterus which normally expel the menstrual fluid.

These substances have been detected during the premenstruum and during menstruation in the circulating blood, but not eight days later.[5]

One of the hormones which increases during menstruation is the essential female sex hormone, estrogen. This hormone leads to an increase in mucopolysaccharides, a complex of carbohydrates. One of the effects that, because of their water-binding capacity, these substances have is upon the vocal cords, causing the latter to retain water and producing minute physiological changes. The result of this, usually some seven to ten days before the onset of menstruation, in some women is the development of a hoarse throat.[6]

The belief in the great powers of menstrual blood were such that, as one might have expected, it was in some cases also endowed with positive powers, not merely negative ones. So it was that in medieval times menstrual blood came to be regarded as a balm against leprosy. Menstrual blood, especially that of young girls, was also considered to be a powerful aphrodisiac. According to the nineteenth-century Italian anthropologist Mantegazza, Louis XIV was a victim of this belief, apparently introduced to it by the Countess de Montespan.

With all the mystery attached to menstruation, women devised all sorts of measures to keep on good terms with it. Deciding (rightly) that the flow must not be stopped, they concluded (wrongly) that they had better avoid ices and iced drinks that might "freeze" the flow. The fact is that iced drinks are warmed up in the stomach and can have no effect on what is going on in other organs. Some women have refrained from changing

[5] V. R. Pickles, *Nature,* Vol. 180 (1957), p. 1198; V. R. Pickles and H. J. Clitheroe, *Lancet,* Vol. 2 (1960), p. 959; O. W. Smith and G. van S. Smith, *American Journal of Obstetrics and Gynecology,* Vol. 54 (1947), p. 201.

[6] M. A. Frable, "Hoarseness: Unrecognized Symptom of Premenstrual Tension," *Archives of Laryngology,* Vol. 75 (1962) p. 66.

their underclothing during or shortly after the menstrual period, thus needlessly doubling the discomfort with which Nature has burdened them. The idea seems to have been that changing one's underthings at this time causes a recurrence of bleeding. This absurd belief has no basis whatever in fact and has been disproven millions of times by the many women who have not fallen victim to it.

Very common among American women is the taboo against taking a bath during the period. There may be some basis for this, as in some women the temperature changes attendant upon bathing causes a temporary intermission in the bleeding; but there is no organic basis for the widespread belief that this delay will affect the mind. The belief, not the delay, is the disturbing factor. Another common belief is that any delay in menstruation, because of bathing or other cause, may result in pregnancy. This is a curious case of wrong-end reasoning: since pregnancy always comes after a halt in menstruation, it is reasoned that any halt in menstruation will inevitably be followed by pregnancy.

Many of the worries and discomforts connected with menstruation would be eliminated with just a thimbleful of education. It is truly astonishing how many adult women are ignorant of the elementary physiology of menstruation, who do not know that their bodies once each month prepare the womb for possible pregnancy by thickening its cellular lining and enriching it with a more abundant blood supply; and that if pregnancy does not occur, the cells lining the womb harden and die, break away, and in doing so, fracture the tiny blood vessels in the wall of the womb, thus causing numerous hemorrhages lasting several days. It is also something of a commentary upon our educational values that most people do not know that this blood is perfectly normal blood, and not some mysterious and poisonous substance.

But perhaps it is not surprising, in view of the fact that nobody took the trouble to give them any instruction at all in the matter and they have depended for all their information on magazine advertisements or random scraps of conversation overheard in washrooms. Despite all the bold talk about the new enlightenment, it is still a fact that sex education in most parts of the United States is in a medieval state. We know of a case of one rather crude woman, whose husband's salary definitely puts her into the middle-class bracket, who deliberately permitted her daughters to enter upon their menstrual periods without either preparing them for it or saying a word to them about what to wear, with the result that the poor girls were utterly bewildered and frightened by the ordeal. "It's more natural for them to learn about it for themselves," this particular mother volunteered. When her daughter reached marriageable age this mother advertised the fact by painting the front house door bright blue. Even where high school courses are given in sex hygiene, the physiology of menstruation is usually presented in such vague terms that it tends to bewilder rather than enlighten the students.

Dr. Hamilton's study of 100 women revealed that 35 had had no instruction as to the meaning and hygiene of menstruation before it occurred. Ten others had heard about it from other children. Two had read about it, and 12 had had some instruction, but an inadequate amount. Only 36 of the 100 women said they had been adequately instructed.

The poor preparation of these women for their entrance into adolescence was evidenced in their descriptions of their feelings when the first menstruation occurred. Eight women said they felt resentment and anger. Eight others described their reaction as "disgust." One said she felt it was a "calamity." Seven others said they felt perplexed—thought it was some sort of accident or that they had injured themselves. Seventeen others described their reaction as "fright." In short, the majority of the reactions described to Dr. Hamilton were characterized by unpleasantness or dread—in a matter which should have been the occasion of healthy pride and rejoicing in one's development.

In a study of 125 American high school girls, Dr. Helen Kennedy, in 1896, referred to the "modesty" which makes it impossible even for mothers and daughters to speak to each other concerning menstrual functions. "Thirty-six girls in this high school passed into womanhood with no knowledge whatever, from a proper source, of all that makes them women. Thirty-nine were probably not much wiser, for they stated they had received some instruction, but had not talked freely on the matter. From the fact that the curious girl did not talk freely of what naturally interested her, it is possible that she was put off with a few words as to personal care, and a reprimand for her curiosity. Less than half the girls felt free to talk with their mothers of this important matter."

In the three-quarters of a century which has elapsed since these observations were reported, there has been some progress, but there can be little doubt that the secrecy with which Victorian mothers enshrouded the "horrid" fact of menstruation is still practiced by too many mothers today.

It frequently happens that it is not the mother's shyness as much as the daughter's which presents the chief impediment to enlightenment. Under such conditions a great deal of tact is necessary if the information is to be transmitted in a satisfactory manner.

The fact is that children should be prepared long before they arrive at puberty in the basic facts relating to development and reproduction.

Many women, particularly those with a vale-of-tears outlook on life, like to think of menstruation as a distinctive suffering which they alone among all species have to bear. Unfortunately, for their self-esteem, they have to share this distinction with the females of apes and many species of monkeys.

There are some women who make a habit of spending several days in bed during their menstrual periods. The reasons they give all boil down to the statement that they are "ill," so that the term "unwell" has, in fact, become a synonym for menstruation. Such women generally belong to the more leisured classes in which the luxury of being bedridden can be enjoyed with immunity. A common explanation offered by such women is that by staying in bed they are able to stave off the process of aging. In point of fact the real reason is much deeper. Such women are attempting to flee from the guilt which they feel during the time when they are considered by society, yes, even our society, to be socially "unclean." They are attempting to flee from the feeling of being a tabooed object and from the frustrations and the aggressions to which those frustrations give rise, which, at such times, makes them "difficult." Upon the lower social levels such women are inclined to demand, for much the same reasons, greater consideration than usual. Under the pressure of their demands for attention they seek to escape the consciousness of the fact that they are really in a condition which requires that they should be avoided. The increased aggressiveness of the female during menstruation is a well-known fact, and in many cases the law recognizes this as an extenuating circumstance in criminal acts committed by such women.

One belief which most people feel sure of is that the first menstruation is a sign of the girl's ability to bear children. That seems logical enough; but it proves that even seemingly logical correlates can be false. The fact is that only rarely is a girl able to conceive immediately after her first menstruation. In the majority of cases, there is a "sterility" period lasting for several months to several years after the first menstruation. It is only at the conclusion of that period that conception is possible (see Chapter 14).

The prizewinning myth about menstruation is that its ebb and flow are controlled by the moon, just as the tides are. This belief seems to have been concocted out of a hash of analogies— the fact that menstruation occurs roughly once a month, approximately the time the moon takes for its phases; the fact that menstruation is a flow, just like the tides; the fact that Diana, the moon goddess, was a virgin, and uninterrupted menstruation is one of the concomitants of virginity. One German writer, A. Gerson, even constructed an ingenious theory to explain the connection between the moon and menstruation. Primitive man, he said, liked to hunt for his females on moonlit nights. The coy wenches fled, but anticipating capture and its consequences, their wombs developed an enriched blood supply. Over the years, this developed into the habit of menstruation.

One of the many troubles with this enchanting "mooning" theory is that the synodical month during which the moon goes through all its phases is about 29½ days long, whereas the menstruation periods of women average from about 28 days to 32 days—with variations from month to month in most women. In fact, irregularity in menstruation is more the rule than the exception, in contrast to the precise habits of the moon.

The time-honored belief in the connection between the phases of the moon and menstruation is enshrined in the very name of that function, *mensis,* meaning month, hence the menses or "monthlies." This alleged connection has been conclusively disproven by three English obstetricians, Drs. D. L. Gunn, P. M. Jenkin, and A. L. Gunn.[7] These investigators examined the menstrual records of no fewer than 10,416 women and found that menstruation in this sizable sample occurred at all times during the month with absolutely no relation whatever to the phases of the moon.

Unfortunately for romance we are forced to the conclusion that the phases of the moon have no more effect on women than do the league baseball schedules.

The general belief that girls in warmer climates menstruate earlier than those in cooler climates is wholly without foundation. In fact, the contrary is true; girls in warmer climates begin to menstruate significantly later than those in cooler climes. The available statistics both for the human female and for the

7 "Menstrual Periodicity," *Journal of Obstetrics and Gynaecology of the British Empire,* Vol. 44 (1937), pp. 839–79.

females of lower animals, as well as for experimentally tested animals under different temperature conditions, proves conclusively that the higher temperatures and humidities have a generally retarding effect upon the development of the reproductive functions—most notably, upon menstruation. American girls born in the Panama Zone, for instance, begin to menstruate later than their sisters born and brought up in the United States.[8]

It may come as a surprise to many people to learn that in spite of the almost universal taboo placed upon menstruating women, and the horror with which menstruation is regarded by men, there are a good many societies in which men actually envy women this function, while at the same time holding it in the greatest fear. In Fiji the men regularly incise the penis in order to let the blood flow from it. In many parts of Australia a very strange operation is performed upon the maturing youth. The whole of his urethra is opened almost from the tip of the penis to the base of the scrotum, and in the opened urethra a stone is inserted to keep it from closing. The native name by which the operated member is called is identical to that for the female vagina. There can be little doubt that this operation originated in the belief that since females possessed a natural means for ridding themselves of the evil humors of the body, and men did not, it was up to the men to imitate the female device by artificial means. At every new initiation the operated men further incise their organs so that the blood may freely flow (see Chapter 24).

[8] See Ashley Montagu, *The Reproductive Development of the Female* (New York: Julian Press, 1957).

14. *Adolescent Sterility*

For many years anthropologists working among non-literate peoples have often observed and been puzzled by the fact that girls who have passed puberty rarely become pregnant despite the experience of frequent intercourse with mature males. It is not merely that such girls rarely give birth, but that they rarely conceive—quite another thing. The question may justly be asked: How is it possible to say with certainty that such girls rarely conceive? May it not be that such girls use effective contraceptive devices? Or if conception does occur, may it not be that they are able to prevent development of the embryo by some abortifacient means?

These are important questions; since they have been investigated they can be satisfactorily answered.

In those nonliterate cultures in which contraception and/or abortion are practiced, it is generally agreed that the contraceptives and abortifacients used are quite ineffective. Himes has made a careful study of the evidence, and this is his conclusion.[1]

Significantly more positive evidence that in nonliterate cultures young postpubertal girls rarely conceive is to be found in those cultures in which there exists a lack of knowledge of the physiological relationship between intercourse and conception.

[1] Norman E. Himes, *Medical History of Contraception* (Baltimore: William & Wilkins Co., 1936).

Such cultures have been studied in Australia and in the Trobri-
and Islands. Contraception is practiced in none of them, while
attempted abortion is rare and usually quite inefficient. Opportunities in such cultures are therefore particularly favorable for
observing the fecundity (physiological capacity to participate in
reproduction) of the female at all ages. Indeed, the fact that
sexually active postpubertal girls do not usually have children
earlier than they have them in Europe was first remarked in
connection with Australian aborigines more than a hundred
years ago. The observation was made by a missionary named
Schurmann and reported by Wilhelmi.[2] Since Schurmann's day
this observation has been often and more precisely made upon
the postpubertal adolescent Australian aboriginal female.

In 1929 Bronislaw Malinowski published his now famous
book *The Sexual Life of Savages,* in which he observed of the
Trobriand Islanders of northwestern Melanesia:

> It is remarkable to note that illegitimate children are very
> rare. The girls seem to remain sterile throughout their period
> of licence, which begins when they are small children and con-
> tinues until they marry; when they marry they conceive and
> breed, sometimes quite prolifically . . . I was able to find roughly
> a dozen illegitimate children recorded genealogically in the
> Trobriands, or about one percent. . . .
>
> Thus we are faced with the question: Why are there so few
> illegitimate children?
>
> . . . Can there be any physiological law which makes conception
> less likely when women begin their sexual life young, lead it in-
> defatigably, and mix their lovers freely? (pp. 166–68).

With these observations Malinowski squarely brought to the
fore the problem of the infertility of the postpubertal girl in
nonliterate societies. Seven years after he posed the problem

[2] C. Wilhelmi, "Manners and Customs of the Australian Natives, in Particular
of the Port Lincoln District," *Transactions of the Royal Society of Victoria,* Vol. 5
(1861), pp. 164–203.

I was fortunate enough to be able to publish its solution.[3] I had been searching for clues to a solution of the problem for some ten years. Malinowski's own suggestions concerning the possible effects of early and indefatigable sexual life and free mixing of lovers could be shown to be irrelevant. The evidence available for nonliterate peoples among whom sexual life commences at an early age shows that they are neither more nor less infecund than those peoples among whom sexual life is begun late. As for free mixing of lovers, this has, from Aristotle's time on, served as an explanation of the sterility of prostitutes. But are prostitutes sterile? Or perhaps it may be more justly inquired: Are they sterile because they mix their "lovers" frequently? Undoubtedly their fertility is low, but this is surely due, among other things, to the preventive measures which they take and to the injurious effects of venereal and other diseases from which they so frequently suffer.

The problem, then, remains. What explanation can there be for the infertility of the sexually active adolescent female? Is it possible that the adolescent infertility of such females is due to a natural and perfectly normal physiological state of relative sterility characteristic of all normal human females during this period of their development, and perhaps also of all physiologically adolescent animals? Or is the phenomenon merely limited to the adolescent females of nonliterate societies? Finally, is it not possible that the phenomenon is a purely specious one?

A survey of the literature proved that the phenomenon was by no means limited to nonliterate societies, was well known to many European gynecologists in the nineteenth century, and was almost certainly not a bogus phenomenon. What then could be the explanation?

The clue for which I had been searching became available in 1930 when L. Mirskaia and F. A. E. Crew of Edinburgh published the results of their investigations on the development of

3 "The Adolescent Sterility Period in Man," *American Journal of Physical Anthropology*, Vol. 21, Suppl. (1936).

"Maturity in the Female Mouse." [4] Mirskaia and Crew studied the development of reproductive capacity in 100 female mice. These were mated at first estrus, that is to say, the period of first heat roughly matching puberty or the first menstruation (menarche) in the human female. These investigators found that pregnancy followed in only 24 cases; 11 pregnancies occurring among the 58 colored mice (19.5 percent) and 13 pregnancies (30.9 percent) among the 42 albino mice. When, however, these same mice were three to six months old, they exhibited a fertility ratio, *i.e.,* the percentage of pregnancies following matings, of 80 to 90 percent. Yet at first estrus only 24 percent of matings resulted in pregnancy. The age at puberty of these mice was: colored, 53 days; albinos, 34 days. Their capacity for efficient reproduction was reached by the third month of life, and between this period and the age of six months, as already noted, pregnancies followed matings in these animals in from 80 to 90 percent of cases. There was a sterile interval, therefore, of some 30 days in the majority of these mice. But as the authors made clear in this study, some 24 percent of the animals were fertile upon first mating at puberty. This is an observation of some importance because it shows that some animals are capable of conceiving at puberty or shortly thereafter. That is to say, the period of adolescent sterility is not necessarily an absolutely sterile one during which conception is impossible in all animals of a group. But one thing did become clear from this and other observations subsequently made by Mirskaia and Crew, namely, that in mice there existed a period of adolescent sterility which could be defined as the interval of time from puberty, and preceding the period of maturity, during which a majority of normally developing mice are incapable of conceiving and remain functionally sterile, while those which do conceive either suffer a high mortality rate or exhibit a high proportion of miscarriages or abortions.

[4] *Proceedings of the Royal Society of Edinburgh,* Vol. 50 (1930), pp. 179–86.

Mirskaia and Crew showed that not only were 76 percent of their mice sterile at puberty, but that of the 24 percent that did conceive, seven, 29.1 percent, died at or immediately following parturition. In addition, four of the albino mice ate their young on the day of birth, such mothers usually dying shortly after devouring their offspring. These figures yield a death rate for pubertal mothers of 45.8 percent, a figure extremely and significantly high.

In the year after Mirskaia and Crew's observations were published, Earle T. Engle of Columbia University published the results of an independent study on mice which served to provide a physiological explanation of the facts recounted by the former investigators. Seventy-two mice ranging in age from seventeen to twenty days were the subjects of these observations.[5] Engle studied the growth of the ovarian follicle in the prepubertal mouse and noted that there were two distinct phases of growth, one from birth to the twelfth day, and the other from the twelfth day to puberty at the thirty-seventh day. On the twelfth day the antrum folliculi (the vesicle containing the ova) is first seen. On the thirteenth and fourteenth days this is slightly augmented, while on the fifteenth day there is a considerable increase in the size of the antral cavity, almost to the size of the follicle at puberty. These observations lead Engle to the conclusion that

> these studies on the ovarian follicle in the 20 days immediately preceding estrus, indicate that these large follicles must be secreting—and liberating—certain amounts of estrin from the 15th day of life, and again emphasize the fact that puberty is a process of slow development, in which the first estrus or first menstruation is merely an incident, expressive of a cumulative action of a delicate hormone balance in the organism. Since the follicles have attained nearly their full size in less than half the life span before puberty, it is clear that the changes occur-

5 "Prepubertal Growth of the Ovarian Follicle in the Albino Mouse," *Anatomical Record*, Vol. 48 (1931), pp. 341–50.

ring, which cannot be morphologically detected, must be those of slow physiological maturation of the organs which operating satisfactorily together, constitute the living animal.

And again:

It is evident that while the interaction of the gonads and the anterior lobe [of the pituitary] affords the physiological mechanism for the first cycle as for the rhythmically succeeding ones, it is evident that this in turn is influenced by somatic factors, and that a general somatic maturity is essential to a complete reproductive potential.

In other words, the presence of ovarian follicles and their secretions is not enough for adequate reproduction. There must be further physiological development before the organism achieves actual reproductive capacity.

Further answers were immediately forthcoming. In the same year, 1931, C. G. Hartman of the Carnegie Institute's Department of Embryology at Baltimore published a brief communication: "On the Relative Sterility of the Adolescent Organism," [6] in which he reported his observations on the Carnegie colony of Rhesus monkeys (*Macacus rhesus*) at Baltimore. In this communication Hartman adduced evidence to show that the generally accepted belief that puberty and maturity or reproductive capacity are equivalent or synchronous phases of development is erroneous. From his study of the evidence he was led to the conclusion that the interval of time which normally elapses between puberty and maturity in man, monkey, and rat is about three years, one year, and one month, respectively.

In his great monograph on the reproduction of the Rhesus monkey published in 1932,[7] Hartman makes it quite clear that

[6] *Science*, Vol. 74 (1931), pp. 226–27.

[7] "Studies in the Reproduction of the Monkey Macacus (Pithecus) rhesus, with Special Reference to Menstruation and Pregnancy, *Carnegie Institute of Washington, Contributions to Embryology*, No. 134 (1932), pp. 1–161.

the failure to ovulate is "the probable cause of the relative sterility of adolescent females." [8]

Later studies by many different investigators have fully confirmed Hartman's observation to the effect that the infecundity of the adolescent organism is primarily due to the fact that the early postpubertal cycles in the female are not usually accompanied by ovulation; hence there can be no fertilization of the ovum, no conception. That this is almost certainly the explanation of the infertility of the postpubertal human female is indicated by the case described by Laqueur of a girl aged twelve years who died from spontaneous intracerebral hemorrhage. This girl was in every way perfectly well developed and was 5 feet 2 inches in height at death. Menarche (the first menstruation) had commenced four months and one week prior to death, and she had experienced four monthly periods. Examination of the ovaries showed the presence of only one degenerating *corpus luteum* (the yellow body on the surface of the ovary through which an ovum has passed), thus indicating that there had been three regularly recurrent menstrual hemorrhages from a healthy uterus without ovulation.[9]

The anatomical findings of these and other investigators indicated some very definite physiological corollaries. Having satisfied myself that the phenomenon of adolescent sterility was a very real one in chimpanzee and man as well as in mouse and macaque, a physiological analysis of the nature of the adolescent sterility period seemed in order. Since my first publication briefly setting out the physiological facts,[10] evidence has become available that such a period also exists in birds. L. E. Richdale's detailed studies on the yellow-eyed penguin (*Megadyptes anti-*

8 See also R. M. Smith and B. Rubinstein, "Adolescence of Macaques," *Endocrinology*, Vol. 26 (1940), pp. 667–79.

9 G. H. Laqueur, "Anatomical Demonstration of the Anovulatory Menstrual Cycle," *California and Western Medicine*, Vol. 63 (1945), pp. 268–69.

10 "Infertility of the Unmarried in Primitive Societies," *Oceania*, Vol. 8 (1937), pp. 15–26, and at greater length in my *Coming into Being Among the Australian Aborigines* (London: Routledge, 1937).

podes) of New Zealand is the first such study which has come to my attention, and as Richdale says, "It would seem that in the Yellow-eyed Penguin and possibly in some other species of birds there is, on the average, a tendency towards sterility with young birds in the period when a small proportion of the individuals are able to breed." The facts, he writes, "resemble closely what has been gathered concerning adolescent sterility in the few mammals studied." [11] The evidence is now clear for two other groups of mammals which have been studied, the sheep [12] and the cow.[13]

In my book *Adolescent Sterility*,[14] I studied at some length the problem bearing upon the reproductive capacities of the human female. The evidence for many different societies was examined, and this showed clearly that the female who is younger than twenty years of age conceives much less easily, as a rule, and much less frequently, in general, than the female after twenty and up to thirty years of age. A high percentage of the younger women are sterile, and prior to the age of twenty years the process of childbearing constitutes a hazard to the life of both mother and child which increases in proportion to the youthfulness of the mother and decreases to a minimum at maturity.

My analysis of the evidence leads to the conclusion that the age of reproductive maturity in the human female is twenty-three *plus or minus* two years. The optimal conditions for reproduction are maintained for about five years, at the end of which time, that is to say between twenty-eight and thirty years

[11] *A Study of a Group of Penguins of Known Age* (Biological Monographs, No. 1, Dunedin, New Zealand, 1949).

[12] H. Goot, "Studies on Some New Zealand Romney Marsh Stud Flocks," *New Zealand Journal of Science and Technology*, Vol 28, No. 1, Sec. A (1946).

[13] L. M. Winters, W. W. Green, and R. E. Comstock, *Prenatal Development of the Bovine* (University of Minnesota Agricultural Experiment Station, Technical Bulletin 151, 1942).

[14] 2d ed., *The Reproductive Development of the Female* (New York: Julian Press, 1967).

of age, the process of involution commences, and at about forty-eight years expresses itself in the menopause. Puberty represents an early transition period in the whole developmental process, during which maturation gradually takes place in certain parts of the reproductive system and leads to the phase of development which we recognize as maturity, the period when the organism actually becomes capable of efficient reproduction. Puberty is the bridge which leads from childhood to maturity.

Let us now turn to a consideration of the biology of adolescent sterility.

In order that a female animal may conceive and bring the process of pregnancy to a successful termination, it is necessary that her ovaries be able to produce mature ova capable of being fertilized, then implanted in the uterus, and there acted upon in such a manner as to cause the fertilized ovum to undergo development up to the stage at which the developed organism is ready for birth. All these processes require the presence in the maternal organism of a number of conditions. Without the presence of any one of these conditions reproduction cannot occur. These conditions come into existence in a definite order in physiological and chronological time, before the establishment of which as a functional complex the female cannot reproduce. If she is not yet able to ovulate, she obviously cannot be impregnated; and if she is able to ovulate, the absence of the interstitial-cell-stimulating hormone (ICSH), or luteinizing hormone (LH), as it is usually called, may make it impossible for the fertilized ovum to become attached to the uterine wall. It is precisely these two conditions, ovulation and formation of the *corpus luteum,* which do not normally become functionally established until some time after puberty, if as in the conventional sense we here take puberty to mean the period of the first estrus or menstruation.

Van Herwerden, as long ago as 1905,[15] and Allen, Hartman,

---

15 M. A. Van Herwerden, *Bydrage Tot de Kennis van Menstrueelen Cyclus en Puerperium* (Dissertation, Utrecht).

Corner, and others since have shown that the early menstrual cycles of the female rhesus monkey are unaccompanied by ovulation. It is thus impossible for the early menstrual rhesus monkey to conceive. I have already indicated that there is good reason to believe that the same holds true for the human female. What happens at puberty is this: As the general process of growth, over which the growth hormone of the anterior pituitary has presided, slows up, this gland pours into the bloodstream a hormone, the follicle-stimulating hormone (FSH), which has the effect, other things being equal, of activating the ovary to elaborate another hormone, estrogen, which is responsible not only for the gradual appearance of the secondary sexual characters but also for the induction of all those changes in the reproductive tract which result in menstruation. Ovulation, however, does not and cannot occur as a result of the action of, or in the presence of, estrogen alone. At puberty estrogen is alone present in appreciable amount. For ovulation to take place another fraction or hormone of the anterior pituitary must come into play, and this is the interstitial-cell-stimulating hormone (ICSH), or as it is better known, the luteinizing hormone (LH). Unfortunately it is not known at what age an amount of luteinizing hormone sufficient to produce ovulation makes its appearance in the blood. Actually it is not quite certain whether the follicle-stimulating hormone and the luteinizing hormone exist as separable fractions or merely represent different states of a single gonadotrophic hormone (*i.e.*, a hormone which acts upon the ovary in the female, and upon the testes in the male), or whether the ovary itself undergoes a series of differential changes for quite other reasons which eventually enable the gonadotrophic hormone to elicit the proper response. But whatever the effects may be, it is known that estrogen, which is alone sufficient to produce those overt phenomena which are collectively termed puberty (briefly, the appearing secondary sexual characters and early menstruation), is not sufficient to produce ovulation. Hence, it is clear that the first or early menstruations must be unassociated with ovulation; and therefore it is impossible for a female, under normal conditions, assuming the nonovulatory character of the early menstruations to be the normal condition, to conceive during the early phase of puberty.

This early or primary phase of puberty is of variable duration in any given population of females, and while it may be under the control of genetic factors, there is some reason to believe that the action of these is subject to modification by environmental conditions.

It is only when the second hormone of the pituitary gland, the luteinizing hormone, is poured into the bloodstream in sufficient quantity, and the ovaries reach the proper stage of differentiation or sensitivity, following the establishment of menarche, that ovulation and impregnation become possible. This is the period of *nubility,* and as more than one earlier author has pointed out, it is not to be confused with the earlier period of puberty.

Evidence of the gradual development of the gonadotrophic excretory activities of the anterior pituitary gland with the approach to and the attainment of adolescence is now available for both sexes. It has been shown that between the ages of three and seven years boys and girls excrete a small and constant amount of estrogens in the urine. From eight to eleven years of age the excretion of estrogens by girls increases, and about one and a half years before menarche it becomes cyclic, the intensity of the cycles gradually increasing. Follicle-stimulating hormone has been detected in the urine of girls as early as eleven years of age, and there is good reason to believe that with the increase in the efficiency of the methods used to determine its presence, follicle-stimulating hormone may be found in girls at still earlier ages. At any rate, it is evident from such findings that menarche represents the culmination of a series of developing endocrine conditions which have been proceeding for some years.

That an appreciable interval of time separates the ability to procreate from the appearance of the first menstruation had already been clearly recognized more than a century ago by such gynecologists as Waddy, Joulin, Matthews Duncan, and others, but the scientific world allowed their suggestive evidence to pass unnoticed. The scientific world was, in fact, quite uninterested in the problem. The problem has become of more general scientific interest only in recent years, and it has remained for modern experimental research in the physiology of sexual development and reproduction of the lower mammals to rediscover and provide the scientific demonstration of the truths first recognized and stated by earlier investigators. Something of the nature of this demonstration we may now briefly resume.

The evidence which we have discussed supports the view that in the females of the mammals thus far investigated—mouse, rat, sheep, cow, macaque, chimpanzee, and man—the ability to reproduce is not, in the large majority of cases, synchronous with the appearance of the first estrus or the first critical expression of puberty, the menarche or first menstruation. The physiological prerequisites of reproduction are ovulation *and* the maintenance of the developing fertilized egg within the uterus. Since these functions do not develop until some time after the advent of the first menstruation, conception and reproduction are, therefore, in most cases, impossible during the menarcheal period. Before ovulation can take place, the endocrine system and the soma must reach a certain degree of development. When this degree of development is attained, ovulation occurs, and this is subsequently followed by the elaboration of two additional hormones, the first being the pituitary luteotrophin and the second progesterone from the *corpus luteum*. It is the reorganizing action of the luteotrophin upon the *corpus luteum* that causes this temporary gland to secrete progesterone. It is progesterone that prepares the uterus for pregnancy. The organism is then said to be *nubile,* the phase of development during which it first becomes viably capable of conceiving and reproducing. Nubility and puberty are phases of development which are often confused with one another, but in reality they represent two very different developmental processes. The interval from the inception of puberty to nubility is termed the adolescent sterility period, the period of adolescence during which the organism continues to be functionally reproductively sterile. Obviously, this interval is not, because of its sterile character, distinguishable from any of the preceding periods of development. It is here merely termed the adolescent sterility period in view of the necessity of emphasizing what appears to be the fact that menarche and the power to procreate are not synchronous events, but that the arrival of the one is separated from the development of the other by an appreciable interval of time, and that this interval represents a period of time during which the organism continues to be functionally sterile. This is not generally recognized to be the case. Menarche, the first menstruation, is most commonly believed to be the sign of the development of the capacity to reproduce, and the only interval at all recognized is that between menarche and maturity, the period of adolescence. Maturity is generally taken to be the period which commences at the time when the growth of the organism comes to an end, in man at about twenty-three plus or minus two years. This view, the evidence indicates, is not sound. The period of adolescence is arbitrarily taken to begin at menarche, but the power to procreate follows only at some time after this physiological function has developed. This is the period of ovarian maturation when ovulation becomes possible, and when conception may follow, the period of nubility. The latter period, nubility, is not coincident with maturity but represents the bridge, as it were, between puberty and maturity, maturity being attained only at an appreciable time after the development of nubility. The period of nubility is not by any means the best time for procreation, for it is a period which is still characterized by high maternal and infant mortality rates. The best time for reproduction is unquestionably at the age of early maturity, when the female organism is fully prepared to undertake and carry through the processes of reproduction satisfactorily.

Adolescent sterility period 13–16 ± 1 year	Puberty	FSH increases by 40 percent Follicular growth First estrus or menarche Anovulatory cycles
Nubility 17–22 ± 2 years		FSH + ICSH (LH) Ovulation Corpus luteum Estrogen
Maturity 23–28 ± 2 years		FSH + ICSH (LH) Ovulation Estrogen Luteotrophin Corpus luteum Progesterone

(THE ITALICIZED HORMONES ORIGINATE IN THE PITUITARY GLAND.)

The Development of Reproductive Capacity in the Female

The physiological basis for the period of adolescent sterility is clear: The duration of the sterility interval in mouse, monkey, chimpanzee, and man would appear to be, respectively, one month, one to twelve months, four months to more than two years, and one month to seven years. Variability in respect of the duration of this period is, of course, the rule, but the precise limits of this variability in any of these groups remains to be determined; nonetheless, it is clear that in the chimpanzee and in man this variability is quite appreciable. In about 25 percent of mice, conception is possible at first estrus, and it has been shown that in all the mammals examined, conception is possible in some animals at first estrus.

The observations of gynecologists and anthropologists would

indicate that in man the interval between menarche and nubility is, on the whole, extremely variable. Certainly, in the human species conception is possible even before the first estrus, and in many such cases the fetus may be carried uneventfully to term, but these are proportionately the exceptional cases. The adolescent sterility period is not one during which conception is impossible. Conception may occur; generally it does not. When it does, the reproductive history of the individuals involved is generally marked by both a high infant and a high maternal death rate or by high spontaneous abortion or miscarriage rates. The evidence we have surveyed indicates that there exists an *absolute* period of adolescent sterility in most females, and that this period, in any given population, is extremely variable in duration.

That a period of adolescent sterility normally exists in most human females is a fact substantiated as much by the observed phenomenon as by the nature of the physiological processes involved in the maturation of the reproductive system. This evidence alone strongly suggests that during early adolescence the organism must, in most cases, necessarily be sterile.

The fact that the existence of such a period of infertility in the postpubertal adolescent female has escaped the attention of most human beings is not as difficult to comprehend as may at first appear. How the belief came into being that the first menstruation represents a token of the female's arrival at the procreative stage of development is not difficult to surmise. It is very likely that it had been independently noted that females remained sterile as long as they had not menstruated, that the first menstruation was followed by periodic menstruation, and that during their menstrual life alone were they capable of bearing children; for after the final cessation of these periods (menopause) they were again sterile. Women capable of menstruation were therefore considered to be capable of childbearing. Hence the advent of menstruation was taken to be the sign of the ability to procreate. The inference is certainly a logical one, but it is for the most part unsound, and unless the conditions are such as to make the observation a simple matter, there is no possible way in which the falsifying factors entering into this inference would become apparent to sense. Since these conditions do not exist in most human societies, it is practically universally believed that the first menstruation is a sign of the ability to procreate. It has been shown here that there is good reason to believe that this is not the case.

It has long been known that the first seminal emissions either contain no spermatozoa [16] or are low in spermatozoa.[17] Since this paper was written, it has been shown that male guinea pigs are characterized by an adolescent sterility period,[18] and Kinsey and his co-workers state that their

> data confirm the previously published work on adolescent sterility in the human female and indicate something of the same sort for the human male. We have a very few records of younger adolescent males being responsible for pregnancies even in groups where coitus is frequent and no form of contraception is employed. Some data exist on the presence of sperm in the first ejaculates of human males, but we are inclined to believe that sperm counts may be too low in the younger human male to effect fertilization. We would emphasize that there must be considerable individual variation on all these matters.[19]

Thus, to the adolescent sterility of the female we have almost certainly to add the adolescent sterility of the male, and thus add further to our understanding the infertility of many adolescent liaisons.

[16] Albert Moll, *The Sexual Life of the Child* (London: Allen & Unwin, 1912), p. 3.

[17] B. T. Baldwin, "The Determination of Sex Maturation in Boys by a Laboratory Method," *Journal of Comparative Psychology,* Vol. 8 (1928), pp. 39–43.

[18] R. C. Webster and W. C. Young, "Adolescent Sterility in the Male Guinea Pig," *Fertility and Sterility,* Vol. 2 (1951), pp. 175–81.

[19] Quoted by Webster and Young, *op. cit.,* p. 180.

15. *Pregnancy and Prejudice*

Most people will hesitate if you ask them the number of furlongs in a mile or how many feet make a fathom, but anybody will tell you with great assurance how long it takes to produce a baby. Nine months, of course. The pregnant woman who goes to her physician will find much the same assurance. He will ask her to name the date of the first day of her last menstrual period, add seven days plus nine months, or a total of 280 days, and tell her the expected day of delivery.

Both the physician's and the layman's computation are the same and roughly correct; the only source of error is the common belief that the length of pregnancy is a precisely established fact. Actually there is a great deal that science does not know about this basic phenomenon, and no physician ever predicted the day of birth except by accident.

In trying to compute the date, there are two things the physician would have to know—and which he doesn't usually know: (1) the date of conception and (2) the duration of gestation.

As for the first, the problem is this: Science has only recently begun to find out anything definite about the timing of human fertilization. Theory after theory has been set up, only to be bowled over by the next one. At present, the most widely accepted theory is that the woman's ovaries ovulate (that is, they discharge an egg cell) at the middle of her menstrual cycle—or roughly about 14 or 15 days after the onset of bleeding. If the woman has had sexual relations the previous day or two, some of the sperm may still be waiting in her uterus or Fallopian tubes and may still be vigorous enough to fertilize the egg as it descends. If there are no sperm waiting, the egg may still be fertilized by intercourse on the day or two following ovulation. After that, the egg starts to disintegrate, and conception is impossible again until the middle of the next menstrual cycle.

That seems simple enough. The only trouble is that there seem to be exceptions. Some scientists believe that the excitement of intercourse may cause ovulation to take place at times other than the middle of the cycle. At any rate, numerous cases have been recorded of conceptions that took place at all parts of the menstrual cycle, including the bleeding period itself. Robert Laton Dickinson, reporting his records on 1,342 women,[1] and S. S. Siegler, summarizing observations on more than 5,000 women,[2] point out that conceptions occur on every day of the 28-day menstrual cycle. In Dickinson's series 13 percent conceived *during* menstruation, while counting from the first day of menstruation most conceptions occurred on the sixth, seventh, and eighth days; 72 percent of conceptions occurred during the first 14 days of the cycle; 20 percent in the third week, and 8 percent in the fourth week.

Under such conditions, how is it possible for the physician to identify the day of conception?

There is one way. Suppose husband and wife were together one day during the month, and the meeting resulted in pregnancy. The physician would know the date of conception exactly—and yet he still couldn't announce the date of birth—not even closely. There are too many variable factors—factors science knows about and factors it is still trying to learn about. For example, Ludwig Nurnberger of Hamburg, Germany, made an ambitious study of duration of pregnancy, in which he claimed to have found that women who indulged in great physi-

[1] *The Control of Conception* (Baltimore: Williams and Wilkins, 1931), p. 52.
[2] *Fertility in Women* (Philadelphia: Lippincott, 1944), pp. 203–4.

cal exertions gave birth an average of twenty days sooner than normal. He also said he found that brunettes gave birth four days sooner than blondes. His findings have not yet been verified by anyone else.

Another variable factor, some scientists say, depends on the sex of the offspring. Boys take longer to be born than girls, according to several studies. P. W. Siegel, a German investigator who made his study during World War I, was able to put his finger on the exact day of conception because the women in his survey were visited by their husbands on 24-hour furloughs. He found that girls were born an average of nine days sooner than boys. His figures indicated birth 276.6 days after conception for boys and 267.6 days for girls. An independent study by a British scientist put girls ahead by five or six days.

But even these findings aren't accepted by all medical scientists.

So the physician's formula of adding 280 days to the start of the last menstruation is just a rule of thumb—and a rough thumb, at that. Actually, only a small minority of the offspring will achieve the birth records on that 280th day. A study by Dr. Ludwig Kraul, of Vienna, involving 8,800 women, showed that only 19.1 percent rang the bell on the 280th day; 37.8 were ahead of schedule, and 43 percent were behind schedule—in most cases by more than a week.

In 3.2 percent of pregnancies, Dr. Kraul reported, pregnancy lasted 300 days or more from the onset of the last menses. This raises the question: Just how long can pregnancy last?

That this is no idle question can be judged from the many lawsuits in Europe and the United States to determine this very point. Usually the motive of the suit is to contest the legitimacy of the offspring in order to prevent him or her from inheriting an estate.

A typical case history is that of the widow of a bookseller, described in 1863 by Dr. W. F. Montgomery, prominent English physician of the last century, in his book *An Exposition of the Signs and Symptoms of Pregnancy.* The erring widow was delivered of a healthy child just 13 months after her husband's death. The baby's legitimacy was questioned in the courts, but the defense produced evidence of her good character. The court ruled that her grief at her husband's death undoubtedly was the cause for this unusual prolongation of pregnancy.

Among the witnesses to her good character was the clerk who operated the bookstore for the widow and married her shortly after she gave birth. This led the skeptical Dr. Montgomery to remark that it is a "very curious coincidence" that in so many cases of unusually protracted pregnancy, the persons involved "should so frequently have been young widows who had been married to old men, with whom they had been childless, and that properties were so generally at stake." There must be, he said, "a special providence in favor of young widows anxious to establish a claim to large fortunes."

But it would not be fair to charge the court with undue gullibility. If they went to the physicians for guidance, they were no better off. In the legitimacy case involving the succession to the Gardner Peerage, heard by the House of Lords in 1825, five prominent physicians testified that gestation lasting much more than 280 days after conception was impossible, whereas twelve other physicians said that pregnancy could occur past the 312th day.

And even in this age of high-powered science, physicians are not in any better position to give a hard and fast answer. Dr. Thomas Watts Eden, a leading British obstetrician, reported in 1923 that he had ascertained six cases in which pregnancy lasted more than 311 days after the last menstruation. The record holder, according to his study, was a woman who gave birth 336 days after the last menses, supposedly 315 days after conception. The offspring weighed 13½ pounds. Remarkable as this case appears, what physician could feel justified in questioning it, or state categorically that pregnancies even longer than this were impossible? Medical science just does not know enough yet about the life of the womb to be dogmatic.

But the law, not worried by scientific problems, finds it very easy to be dogmatic. Guttmacher cites statutes from the legal codes of several countries bearing on this problem. A Scottish law says that a child born more than ten months or 300 days after the departure of the woman's husband is automatically considered illegitimate. The Code Napoleon included a similar rule, holding that a child born more than 300 days following the death or departure of the husband could have his legitimacy contested, although he was not automatically to be considered illegitimate. The Prussian lawmakers were a bit more lenient; they set the grace period for the women at 302 days after her husband's death or departure. The Austrians were even kinder; they raised it to 307 days.

The *Multeka ul ubbur,* the religious and moral statute book of the Turks, holds that pregnancy can last from six to twenty-four months.

Folk beliefs in various parts of the world are even more charitable than the laws. For example, the old Chinese book *Dan-zi-nan-fan* says pregnancy can last as long as two years. Aristotle remarked that people of his day believed pregnancy could last as long as eleven months, but he didn't believe it. Pliny, more credulous, tells about a thirteen-month delivery.

A report from Morocco relates that there is a saying among Moorish women that a child can sleep in the womb for years. Thus if a widow or divorced woman gives birth two or three years after separation from her husband, she says the child has just "awakened."

The opposite belief has been reported among some of the southern Slavic peoples. There it is possible for a woman to give birth to a fully developed child six weeks after marriage without causing a scandal. The simple explanation is that it was a high-speed gestation.

The medieval Talmudic savants believed that pregnancy

could be prolonged up to twelve lunar months. A story comes down from fourteenth-century Austria of a Talmudic student named Schlemiel who left his home to pursue his studies at a foreign school and came back eleven months later to find his wife about to give birth. Much disconcerted by this phenomenon, Schlemiel ran to his spiritual mentors for guidance, and they told him that overlong pregnancy was fully possible. Ever since then, the word "schlemiel" has been used to describe a poor, gullible fool.

Dr. G. L. Park, in a study of 2,100 women seen in his practice during the course of many years, found that 32 percent delivered before the expected date and 68 percent on or after the expected date of delivery; 31 percent during the forty-first week, 26 percent during the forty-second week, 8.5 percent during the forty-third week, and 2.5 percent during the forty-fourth week. The peak period appears to be the end of the forty-first week and the beginning of the forty-second week, that is, the seventh, eighth, and ninth day after the expected day of delivery. The majority of births, 57 percent, occur during the forty-first and forty-second weeks. But in fact Park found that 20.9 percent of his cases delivered in the fortieth week, before the expected day of delivery. In short, 78 percent delivered between the fortieth and forty-second week, which would make the average somewhere about the forty-first week; note, *not* forty-one weeks but the *forty-first* week. Park suggests that it would be more reasonable to calculate the expected day of conception by taking the first day of the last menstrual period and adding fourteen instead of seven days. This would mean 41 weeks after the first day of the last period and would also mean approximately 39 weeks from conception.[3]

In reality it is now known that the average duration from conception to delivery in the human species is 266½ days or 38 weeks, so the evidence suggests that obstetricians would do well

[3] G. L. Park, "The Duration of Pregnancy," *Lancet*, Vol. 2 (1968), pp. 1388–89.

to think not in terms of 280 days but in terms of the realities. In this way they will avoid judging perfectly normal cases as either immature or postmature.

One of the most curious errors regarding pregnancy was fathered by Hippocrates, about 2,500 years ago, who asserted that the embryo grows head upward in the womb and that suddenly, during the last days of pregnancy, it turns upside down. Aristotle repeated this error a hundred years later. Somehow it cropped up among the Hindus; in fact, Susruta, the great Indian physician who is said to have lived in the sixth century B.C., had already written down the same assertion in the *Ayur-Veda*. The Hebrew Talmud said the same. The midwifery books of medieval Germany carried it along, and Mauriceau, the great seventeenth-century French gynecologist, accepted it without question. When dissection of corpses began, young embryos were often found in the womb head down. But these findings were considered exceptions. They conflicted with the great Hippocrates, and when observation conflicts with dogma, it is only the boldest man who sticks by his observation.

Today, of course, it is known that the embryo usually grows with the head down (due to gravity), not up, and that although the embryo does sometimes radically shift its position, this is far from being the universal rule promulgated by all the ancient "authorities."

But even today, the belief in the sudden overturn of the fetus still survives in some places. It has been reported among the Chinese and Japanese.

Another old myth that has had a hardy life is the belief that rubbing the body with ointments will make things easier for the pregnant woman. The physicians of ancient Rome advised their women patients to rub their bodies with fat during the ninth month of pregnancy. The same prescription has been common in India from the oldest recorded times to the present. Ambroise Paré, the great sixteenth-century French surgeon, recommended rubbing fat into the thighs and genitals to make confinement easier. An old custom in Russian Astrakhan was to rub the abdomen with oil or butter. Curiously, the tradition is even found in the Tonga Islands, where women use oil and curcuma, a starchy root, and in the Dutch East Indies, where pregnant women rub their bodies twice a day with crushed pine leaves.

In the United States, belief in the value of massage with ointments for preserving the figure is very common, physicians report. Most physicians are skeptical of its value, but if the patient feels strongly about it, the doctor prescribes something non-injurious, such as cocoa butter, to keep her happy. Dr. Alan Guttmacher tells of a patient who developed a skin eruption over her entire abdomen from using patent medicine guaranteed to prevent "the streaks of pregnancy." Dr. Guttmacher also cites some other bits of American mythology he picked up during his service in the maternity wards of Johns Hopkins Hospital. One woman told him her mother-in-law had warned her against high heels because they would make the child cross-eyed.

Another woman, whom Dr. Guttmacher describes as a "very intelligent patient, the wife of a physician," asked him if it was dangerous to raise her arms above her head. A friend of her mother's had told her that the embryo might be strangled in its umbilical cord if she did that. This belief is very interesting, because it can be found, with variations, in many parts of Europe. Esthonian women, when pregnant, avoid making circular movements while washing clothes, for fear they will make the umbilical cord twist around the child. For the same reason, pregnant women in Franconia, Germany, creep under a rope or a plank; and in the Palatinate pregnant women avoid creeping under a clothesline or weaving or twisting yarn. And skipping to the Babar Islands of the Dutch East Indies, we find that the pregnant women aren't supposed to weave cloths or mats.

Another American myth reported by Dr. Guttmacher also has worldwide distribution. It is that sexual intercourse during pregnancy is harmful. Dr. Guttmacher's patient said she had been told that such behavior would make the child "oversexed." This reason seems purely an American idea. Other peoples who forbid intercourse during pregnancy have other reasons—mostly a vague feeling that it would injure the embryo or expose it to danger. Coitus with a pregnant woman is forbidden in the Malay Archipelago, among the Ashanti and Basutos of Africa, and among many Chinese groups. On Yap, in the Caroline Islands, the husband must keep separate from his wife until eight or ten months after she gives birth.

The ancient Medes and Persians strictly forbade intercourse during pregnancy. The Hebrew Talmud warned that it was dangerous during the first three months but all right during the next three months and positively beneficial during the last three months.

Although some physicians advise complete abstinence, the advice of most physicians with regard to this question is: If there is no history of previous miscarriage or bleeding during pregnancy, sexual intercourse is permissible until six weeks from term. After that, intercourse is dangerous because the mouth of the womb tends to open somewhat and intercourse might introduce dangerous bacteria.

Despite this, there is a belief among some Americans that intercourse during the early stages of labor makes birth easier, because the semen "lubricates" the vaginal canal. This practice has resulted in fatal cases of puerperal fever.

A belief one hears expressed again and again is that the fetus sleeps all day and picks the night to start kicking. Pregnant women vow that the fetus takes a "malicious" delight in keeping them from sleeping. Actually, the fetus lives completely in the dark and cannot tell the time. If it seems to move more at night, it is only because the woman is more likely to feel its slight movement while lying in a quiet room without anything to distract her.

Some women whose impulse to gluttony is curbed most of

the time by a concern about their figures really let themselves go during pregnancy. Since they are going to grow heavier anyway, they reason, they might as well go whole hog—literally. They justify their gluttony by saying they "have to eat for two." This fallacy has long been outmoded by medical science. The amount of food needed to sustain the mother will take care of the fetus, too. In fact, in cases in which the woman is overweight to start with, the physician may actually put her on a diet during pregnancy.

Another old chestnut some women still like to repeat is: "Every child a tooth." Maybe that was true before we knew anything about diet. Now, of course, any woman can discover, by the mere process of asking a physician, what she should eat to make sure she obtains enough calcium, so the fetus won't have to rob her teeth and bones of calcium to build its body. Most physicians will advise a minimum intake of a pint of milk a day.

Some women think that a bad tooth should not be extracted during pregnancy. Why they hold this belief is not clear. There is an old German superstition that if a pregnant woman has a tooth pulled, her child will be born with a malformed back. But there is no more scientific basis for this belief than there is for most of the others. If a general anesthetic is administered to the mother to deaden the pain during extraction, this might upset the fetus, as might a local anesthetic. Anesthetics, in general, should be avoided during pregnancy, unless they are very light ones, because they tend to reduce the oxygen circulating to the fetus.

One of the oldest tenets of the American credo is that discomforts and complications of pregnancy and childbirth are purely the results of civilization, and that "savages" have their babies with no more to-do than when getting a haircut. Men particularly like to cite this bit of popular anthropology, in reproof of the moans of their helpmeets. They love to tell the classic story of the Indian woman who, while on the march with her tribe, steps for a moment into the bushes, gives birth to her baby, and then comes out and falls into line again.

Any visitor to the so-called primitive communities of the world knows this picture of painless pregnancy and parturition is not altogether true. For example, a traveler among the Sinaugolo of New Guinea reports the common occurrence of morning sickness. In the Fiji Islands, midday vomiting and attacks of giddiness are common. Practically everywhere in the world, one finds amulets and other magic devices for assuring the pregnant woman a safe and easy outcome.

Equally false is the belief that the husband in all primitive tribes hardly gives a thought to his wife's pains and lets her slave away until the baby is ready to be born. Although in some tribes the woman does not receive very much attention, in others the husband is even more considerate than many good solid Americans. In the Caroline Islands, the husband relieves his wife of her work as soon as he knows she is pregnant and waits on her from then on. Among the Annamites of Indo-China, the woman is relieved of household chores starting in the sixth and seventh month. In the Mentawei Islands in Indonesia, the husband does the dishes and other household chores and encourages his wife to relax on the veranda.

In fact, some of these peoples actually err on the side of indulgence. Most obstetricians believe that a continuation of normal activity up to the very last week of pregnancy will result in an easier confinement.

A not uncommon belief is that nonwhite women who have conceived by a white man experience greater difficulties in giving birth than they do with children who are the offspring of men of their own ethnic group. It has been seriously argued that because the black female has a narrower pelvis than the white female she is less likely to experience a satisfactory termination to a pregnancy produced by a white male than to one produced by a black male. The implied suggestion here is that the rounder-headed white is likely to produce a fetus which will have a head larger and rounder than can be safely delivered through a small, narrow pelvis "intended" for the delivery of black-fathered children.

Caldwell and Moloy have, from the obstetrical viewpoint, investigated the measurable traits of the pelvis of black and white females.[4] These investigators find that female pelves may be classified into three types: (*a*) the gynecoid, or average female type, which occurs in 42 percent of black females and in the same percentage in white females; (*b*) the android type, more closely approximating the male form than the female pelvis, which occurs in 15.7 percent of Negro females and in 32.5 percent of white females; and (*c*) the anthropoid type, with a long anteroposterior diameter and a relatively narrow transverse diameter, occurring in 40.5 percent of blacks and in slightly less than half that percentage of whites.

Obstetrically, the most dangerous form of pelvis is the android type, which occurs among white females with double the frequency that it occurs among black females. The other two types of pelvis present no especial obstetrical difficulties. It therefore seems improbable that the form of the black pelvis plays any more significant role in difficult labor and delivery than in the case of the white females.

Davenport and Steggerda, in a study of ethnic crossing in Jamaica, "entertained the hypothesis that, in the case of the black woman who carried a mulatto child *in utero,* her narrow pelvic outlet and the child's large head might offer an important disharmony."[5] In order to test this hypothesis they proceeded to examine the heads of newborn colored and white children. They found that the heads of the newborn colored infants were slightly smaller at birth than those of white newborn infants, and it is evident from their findings that no disharmonies be-

[4] W. E. Caldwell and H. C. Moloy, "Anatomical Variations in the Female Pelvis and Their Effects in Labor, with a Suggested Classification," *American Journal of Obstetrics and Gynecology,* Vol. 26 (1933), pp. 479–514.

[5] C. B. Davenport and Morris Steggerda, *Race Crossing in Jamaica* (Washington, D.C.: Carnegie Institute of Washington, 1929), pp. 423–24.

tween pelvic outlet and shape of head occurred in the Jamaica series examined by these investigators.

Alleged disharmonies of this sort have been claimed to exist as a result of the union of Japanese women with white men. This matter was thoroughly investigated by the United States Army Medical Corps in Japan, in 500 cases in which a Japanese woman was married to a white, and led to the unequivocal conclusion: "The Japanese woman married to a Caucasian was found to present no greater difficulties in obstetric management than the Caucasian counterpart." [6]

In the face of the extremely low maternal and infant mortality rates of the Hawaiian population, in which so many offspring of mixed marriages are born, and what we know of the black-white experience, the notion of interethnic birth disharmony seems to be quite without foundation.

[6] C. W. Sargent, C. H. Westfall, and F. M. Adams, "The Obstetric Risk of the Japanese Woman with a Caucasoid Husband," *American Journal of Obstetrics and Gynecology*, Vol. 76 (1958), pp. 137–40.

16. *Maternal Impressions*

Many a woman whose child is born with a birthmark will tell you with great certainty how one day, midway in her pregnancy, she was frightened by something or other and thereby marked her child. In telling you that, she is uttering one of the most ancient of all beliefs—that mental impressions of the pregnant woman will affect the child, physically or mentally.

The ancient Hindu women, for example, were told by Susruta, the great Hindu physician of the sixth century B.C., to avoid touching deformed persons, and the Chinese were warned against letting a pregnant woman see hares, mice, hedgehogs, tortoises, frogs, otters, and toads. In the thirteenth century Pope Martin IV ordered all the heraldic decorations removed from his residence because the coat of arms contained a bear which had so frightened a lady of the court that she gave birth to a hairy infant.

In ancient Prussia there was a folk regulation that if a woman met a cripple, she was to look at once up at heaven or at her fingernails.

In Transylvania pregnant women are told that if they encounter something frightful, they are to grasp their buttocks and say, "I am not afraid." This saves the unborn infant from being marked.

The belief in the dangers of unpleasant impressions has a

natural corollary in a belief in the value of pleasant ones. Many an American woman in the expectant state will drag herself from symphony concert to art exhibit in the hope that aesthetic contemplation will create an aesthetic-looking child. This belief can be traced back to the ancient Chinese, who, according to one old book, had songs and "proper stories" read to an expectant mother. "Thus," says the book, the *Siao-hio,* "a well-made and clever child was born."

The sad story of one believer in this myth is told by Drs. Costler and Willy in the *Encyclopaedia of Sexual Knowledge.* A woman of their acquaintance spent whole days before the paintings in the Louvre so that her child would "have the face of an angel." Unfortunately, the baby was born hydrocephalic and died in two days.

In ancient Greece the laws of Lycurgus compelled pregnant Spartan women to look constantly at the statues of Castor and Pollux, which represented strength and beauty.

The belief in the effect of maternal impressions is quite understandable, because of the close association of fetus and mother. While it is true that there is no direct connection between the nervous system of the mother and that of the fetus, and while it is also true that there is no connection directly between their bloodstreams, there nevertheless is an indirect connection between them. This is through the neurohumoral system, that is to say, the interacting nervous and endocrine glandular systems through the fluid medium of the blood. Therefore the nervous states of the mother actually can influence the developing fetus; but this is a very different thing from saying that the mother's mental states are capable of making a musician or an artist of her child as a consequence of her symphonic and artistic activities during pregnancy.

The blood of the mother is filtered through the placenta so that practically none of her original blood reaches the fetus; what filters through are the necessary nutriments necessary for the nourishment of the fetus—but there is no actual mixing of bloods. In spite of this fact, which has been demonstrated again and again, the old belief is still widespread, even among educated persons. For example, many a pregnant woman will refuse to eat a double plum or peach for fear it will cause her to have twins, that somehow the doubleness will have gotten through in the blood.

Which recalls the fact that the King of Siam forbade the original Siamese twins from appearing in public because he feared the sight of them would cause pregnant women to produce similar monstrosities. The French government forbade them to tour France for the same reason.

The belief in maternal impressions has had a long life among medical men and was seriously discussed in learned journals not very long ago. Theophilus Parvin outlined the controversy in *The Science and Art of Obstetrics* (1895). He pointed out that the philosopher Herbert Spencer believed in it, and half a dozen prominent American physicians went on record in its favor. He tells of five cases recounted to him by physicians, including the story of a woman who watched a performance of a mathematical prodigy while she was pregnant and gave birth to a child who was brilliant at mathematics.

The *Boston Medical and Surgical Journal* in 1839 reported, over the signatures of eight physicians, the case of Robert H. Copeland, twenty-nine years old, who had a face like a snake, and coiled and uncoiled his arm like a snake—all because a rattler had tried to bite his mother during her sixth month of pregnancy. It is very possible that Oliver Wendell Holmes got the idea for his novel *Elsie Venner* from this report, for in that novel he tells the story of a girl whose mother was actually bitten by a snake during her pregnancy. When the girl grew up she was a great beauty, but her expression, her eyes, and her temperament were fatally like those of a snake.

Sir Walter Scott, the great novelist, told of a lady whose father, before her birth, had been under sentence of death; she consequently was "marked on the back of the neck by the sign of a broadaxe." The story occurs in Scott's *Redgauntlet* and may be regarded as an example of *paternal* impression. The *Berakoth Tractate* of the Talmud tells of a vain fellow named Rabbi Jochanan, who made a practice of sitting near the door of the public baths. He explained, "When the daughters of Israel come out of the bath, they may look upon me, so that they may get children who are as beautiful as I."

Of all the maternal impressions, the most potent ones in affecting the offspring are the "longings." The expectant mother wants to eat all sorts of bizarre foods, especially hard-to-get or expensive ones. We hear such stories not only in our pampered civilization but also among nonliterate peoples.

What is the source of these dietary longings? The question cannot be answered with certainty. Some physicians believe that they are fictitious; the woman is merely taking advantage of her pregnant state to indulge her wish to be pampered. Others believe the origin is the actual craving of the body for food elements required by the growing fetus. There is no question that the pregnant woman's physiology is altered and that all sorts of imbalances are going to occur from time to time, and it is conceivable that cravings for certain foods might be an expression of the body's attempt to right itself. But skeptics laugh off that argument by saying it is mostly the rich who have these cravings; the impoverished woman, who couldn't hope to get peacock tongues or fresh strawberries in January, rarely develops a craving for them.

So widespread is the belief in the reality of these strange urges that a pregnant woman who doesn't have them is, in some circles, considered *déclassée*. At the very least, her friends will say, she should have an impulse to devour asparagus or ice cream. To have no craving at all is—well, it's simply not done!

Havelock Ellis cites the story of the Duchess d'Abrantès, who, though well advanced in pregnancy, never had any longings for strange foods. "No cravings?" said her mother. "This is impossible. I shall certainly speak to your mother-in-law." The two old ladies went to work on her. They explained that *every* pregnant woman had cravings, and that stifling these urges was very dangerous—it could make a monster of the child. Her husband began to ask her anxiously if there was anything she longed for. Her sister-in-law told her all sorts of stories about children being born with marks because the mothers had unsatisfied longings. So the Duchess began to wonder what she ought to long for. One day it occurred to her that she had never eaten pineapple. She asked for one. It was the wrong season. There was none in all Paris. The Duke scoured the city in vain. She then felt that she had to have a pineapple or she couldn't live. The Duke finally obtained one through the good offices of Madame Bonaparte. He rushed home with it in triumph that night. The family doctor warned the Duchess not to eat it until morning. So she spent the night hugging the pineapple. But when she tried to eat it in the morning, it nauseated her.

"The Duchess adds that ever since then, although she liked the flavor of pineapple, she could never eat one without forcing herself," Ellis concludes. "We might add further that she became insane in her old age."

The belief that unsatisfied cravings will produce birthmarks or deformities in the offspring has led lawmakers of many lands to be indulgent toward pregnant larcenists. For example, a law passed during the French Revolution enabled mothers-to-be who were caught stealing to plead that they acted from an irresistible impulse. (Napoleon, a mean old misogynist, repealed it.) A law of Rommersheim, Germany, dated 1298, gave special permission to pregnant women to fish in a stream belonging to the landowner. The rabbis of the Talmud authorized pregnant women who felt intense cravings for foods to break the fast of Yom Kippur, holiest day in the Jewish calendar. Anthropologists who studied the American Indians during the last century told of cases in which a husband took 40- or 50-mile hikes to procure for his pregnant spouse the dish of cranberries or bowl of maize she hankered after.

The widespread superstition that if the woman couldn't secure the thing she longed for, she should slap her buttocks in
order to prevent her unborn child from being marked has led
to at least one interesting report. This powerful magic very
unhappily failed to work in the case of a Mrs. Wilkins of Cin-
cinnati. As reported by Miller in the *Obstetrical Gazette* in
1881, the poor woman had a longing for oysters which couldn't
be satisfied. She slapped herself dutifully on the buttocks; but
some months later she gave birth to a child marked with a birth
blemish that looked very much like an oyster. It was on his
buttocks, by the way.

One of the most frequent birthmarks is the glowing red mark
called the "strawberry mark." Its resemblance to the color of
the strawberry undoubtedly is the reason so many American
women attribute its occurrence to their unsatisfied longing for
that expensive delicacy. In Europe, however, where strawberries
aren't so popular, the same blemish is called a "wine mark,"
and the good folk say it is due to an unsatisfied longing for wine.

This belief was critically examined back in the seventeenth
century by François Mauriceau, the great French obstetrician.
He pointed out that in parts of Italy and France where only
white wine is drunk, one would expect children to be born with
white birthmarks; but red marks were just as common there as
elsewhere. The actual fact was, he said, that these marks had
nothing to do with longings; they were simply due to a birth
injury—a slight hemorrhage beneath the skin causing an indel-
ible red stain.

Mauriceau published these observations in 1668. Nevertheless, people in both Europe and the United States still believe
the red marks come from longings.

Guttmacher tells the sad story of Camerarius, seventeenth-
century botanist, whose wife was suddenly inflamed by a desire
to hit somebody with the eggs she had just brought from the
market. Not wanting to have his unborn offspring marred by
letting this powerful urge go unsatisfied, the scientist obligingly

held a cloth in front of his face while his wife tossed the eggs at him.

Many of the ancients believed that the unborn child could be affected by mental influence not only during pregnancy but also at the moment of conception. Thus the Talmudists told the following story in the *Midrash Bereshith Rabba:*

> There was once a Moor who married a Moorish woman and begot a white son by her.
>
> The father took the son and came to the rabbi and spake thus: "This is perhaps my son."
>
> Then the rabbi asked him: "Hast thou images in thine house?"
> "Yes."
> "Are they black or white?"
> "White."
> "Hence," said the rabbi, "thou hast the white son."

Ambroise Paré, the sixteenth-century French surgeon, tells the story of his book *Of Monsters and Prodigies* (1573): "Damascen reports that he saw a maid hairy like a bear, which had that deformity by no other cause or occasion than that her mother earnestly beheld, in the very instant of receiving and conceiving the seed, the image of St. John covered with a camel's skin, hanging upon the posts of the bed."

The belief in the efficacy of pleasant impressions influencing the child has truth on its side to this extent: the pleasanter the mother's experiences during pregnancy, the better are the chances of the fetus developing as it should. Furthermore, a happy frame of mind in the pregnant mother will encourage good general health and thus benefit the fetus.

17. Climate and Reproduction

The myth that so-called "primitive" peoples are often characterized by a breeding season or seasonal sterility dies hard. Some years ago Whitaker [1] showed how unsound this claim was regarding the Eskimos, of whom it was often made. Westermarck in a discussion of the subject cited some two hundred references in support of the theory that the ancestors of modern man were characterized by a circumscribed pairing or breeding season. [2] The notion that the periods at which the greatest number of births occur among the human species indicate the survival of a primitive human sexual rhythm associated with "annual changes in the human organism especially connected with the sex function" was discussed very fully by Havelock Ellis many years ago. [3] These ideas find a place in the works of such distinguished physiologists as Marshall [4] and Wright, [5] and they have found a vigorous supporter in a leading student of population. [6]

Such authors have assumed that since the Catarrhine monkeys and the anthropoids are characterized by a pairing season,

[1] W. L. Whitaker, *Science*, Vol. 88 (1938), p. 214.
[2] E. Westermarck, *The History of Human Marriage*, Vol. II (1922), p. 76; *The Future of Human Marriage* (1936), p. 10.
[3] H. Ellis, *Studies in the Psychology of Sex*, Vol. II (1900), p. 88.
[4] F. H. A. Marshall, *The Physiology of Reproduction* (1910), p. 672.
[5] S. Wright, *Applied Physiology* (1934), p. 198.
[6] A. M. Carr-Saunders, *The Population Problem* (1922), p. 92.

the ancestors of modern man must likewise have been so characterized and that certain nonliterate peoples still exhibit evidences of this "ancestral trait." It so happens that the major
premise of this syllogism is a pure assumption without the
slightest factual foundation, for the evidence is quite clear and
unequivocal that neither the Catarrhine monkeys nor the anthropoid apes are characterized by a breeding season, but that
they are capable of breeding and of copulating at all times.[7]
The statements of travelers and of other occasional observers
concerning the existence of an alleged breeding or rutting
season among certain so-called primitive peoples could be cited
ad nauseam, but there is one that has been so often quoted
by those who have put their faith in a human breeding season,
and which is so typical of all such statements, that it deserves
to be given here together with the sort of evidence which puts
such statements in the category to which they properly belong.
Westermarck [8] begins his citation of the evidence in support
of the existence of a breeding season in primeval man with the
statement: "According to Mr. Johnston, the wild Indians of
California, belonging to the lowest races on earth, have their
rutting seasons as regularly as have the deer, the elk, the ante-
lope, or any other animals.[9] With reference to some of these
Indians, Mr. Powers says that spring 'is a literal Saint Valen-
tine's Day with them, as with the natural birds and beasts of
the forest.' " [10] When we consult our greatest authority on the
California Indians for some light on these matters, we find him
writing of the Yurok, a Californian people who live along the

---

[7] For a discussion of the evidence which it is impossible to cite here see M. F.
Ashley Montagu, *Coming into Being Among the Australian Aborigines* (1937),
p. 258.

[8] *Loc. cit.,* p. 81.

[9] A. Johnston, "The California Indians," in H. R. Schoolcraft, *Historical and
Statistical Information Respecting the History, Condition, and Prospects of the
Indian Tribes of the United States,* Vol. IV (1860), p. 224.

[10] S. Powers, "Tribes of California," in *Survey of the Rocky Mountain Region*
(1877), p. 206.

reaches of the lower Klamath River; they are characterized by an excessive desire for wealth and the great regard in which they hold money, which circulates among them in the form of dentalium shells.

> The significant fact is that they hold a strong conviction that the dentalium money and the congress of the sexes stand in a relation of inherent antithesis. This is one reason given for the summer mating season: the shells would leave the house in which conjugal desires were satisfied, and it is too cold and rainy to sleep outdoors in winter.... Births occurred among the Yurok and their neighbors chiefly in spring. This was, of course, not because of any animal-like impulse to rut in a certain season, as has sometimes been imagined, but because of highly specialized ideas of property and magic.... Since dentalia and other valuables were kept in the house, a man never slept there with his wife. ... The institution of the sweat house rendered this easily possible. In summer, however, when the cold rains were over, the couple made their bed outdoors; with the result that it seems natural to the Yurok that children should be born in spring.[11]

Thus, when the superficial observations of the older observers are interpreted in the light of the facts, they are seen to have a meaning quite different from that which has rather loosely been attributed to them.

In later years, as a result chiefly of Rowan's work [12] on artificial illumination and sexual periodicity,[13] an attempt has been made to bolster up the breeding season myth in the special case of the Eskimo.[14] Whitaker has shown the unsatisfactory

11 A. L. Kroeber, "Handbook of the Indians of California," *Bureau of American Ethnology Bulletin*, Vol. 78 (1925), p. 41.

12 W. Rowan, *Nature*, Vol. 115 (1925), p. 494; *Nature*, Vol. 120 (1928), p. 11; *Proc. Bost. Soc. Nat. History*, Vol. 38 (1926), p. 147; *Proc. Bost. Soc. Nat. History*, Vol. 39 (1929), p. 151.

13 For a review of the literature dealing with this subject see T. H. Bissonnette, *Quart. Rev. Biol.*, Vol. 11 (1936), p. 371, and Rowan's paper, "Light and Reproduction," *Biol. Rev.*, Vol. 13 (1938), p. 374.

14 Ll. J. Llewellyn, *Nature*, Vol. 129 (1932), p. 868.

nature of the evidence upon which this attempt was based. In passing it may be remarked here that Rowan's work has been very generally misunderstood as proving that light *qua* light is the causative factor in producing gonadal development, whereas what Rowan has actually claimed to have shown is that it is more probably the effect of light, namely, *wakefulness,* which produces the observed effect.[15]

Now, while it is certain that no human beings are characterized by a circumscribed period of reproduction, there exists a certain amount of evidence which very strongly suggests that climatic factors do affect the reproductive capacity of most vertebrates, including man. Thus, for example, the breeding seasons of various birds and mammals can be shown to be correlated with certain seasons, and when these animals are removed from the Northern to the Southern Hemisphere, or vice versa, they adapt themselves after a short time to the reversed calendric seasons and come into estrus (heat) in the season in which they formerly did, although in different months. This has been shown in the case of birds,[16] and for the mammals thus far investigated.[17] For the distribution in the incidence of conceptions in the primates with a high relative sterility and menstrual disturbance in the summer months this seasonal correlation has been shown to hold good in the case of the Rhesus monkey,[18] and also for man.[19] The high frequency of disturbances of the menstrual cycle during the summer months in young and adult women has been reported by many investigators,[20] and it is also of some interest to note that the greatest

[15] W. Rowan, *Proc. Zool. Soc. London*, Ser. A, Vol. 108, Pt. 1 (1938), p. 51.

[16] J. R. Baker and R. M. Ranson, *Proc. Zool. Soc. London*, Ser. A, Vol. 108, Pt. 1 (1938), p. 101.

[17] F. H. A. Marshall, *Proc. Roy. Soc.*, 122 B (1937), p. 413.

[18] C. G. Hartman, *Contrib. Embryol.*, No. 134 (1932), p. 39.

[19] C. A. Mills and F. A. Senior, *Arch. Int. Med.*, Vol. 46 (1930), p. 921.

[20] E. T. Engle and M. C. Shelesnyak, *Human Biol.*, Vol. 6 (1934), p. 431; E. Allen, *Am. Jour. Obst. and Gynec.*, Vol. 25 (1933), p. 705; C. F. Fluhman, *Am. Jour. Obst. and Gynec.*, Vol. 26 (1933), p. 642; J. L. King, *Am. Jour. Obst. and Gynec.*, Vol. 25 (1933), p. 583.

number of abortions appears to occur during the summer months.[21]

Apart from the evidence provided by the lower vertebrates, the fact that the lowest number of conceptions, the greatest number of menstrual irregularities, and the greatest number of abortions occur in the human species wherever investigated during the summer months indicates that the reproductive life of man is in some way influenced by climatic factors. That these factors are probably fairly complex should, for methodological purposes at least, be assumed, for it now seems unlikely that any one single factor such as light or temperature alone can be considered as the sufficient cause of these reproductive phenomena. The low summer conception rates among the Eskimo of Greenland as given by Bertelsen [22] and referred to by Whitaker is yet another illustration of this apparently universal relation between low reproductivity and the summer months. What the nature of this relation is here, as elsewhere, is a problem which remains to be investigated. The purpose of the present communication is to make it clear that such a relation exists.

[21] W. Millar, *Human Biol.,* Vol. 6 (1934), p. 279.
[22] A. Bertelsen, *Meddelelser om Grønland,* Vol. 117, No. 1 (1935).

18. *The Origin and Significance of Neonatal and Infant Immaturity in Man*

Why are human beings born in a state so immature that it takes eight to ten months before the human infant can even crawl and another four to six months before he can walk and talk? That a good many years will elapse before the human child will cease to depend upon others for his very survival constitutes yet another evidence of the fact that man is born and remains more immature for a longer period than any other animal.

The newborn elephant and the fallow deer can run with the herd shortly after they are born. By the age of six weeks, the infant seal has been taught by his mother to navigate his watery world for himself. These animals all have long gestation periods, presumably because animals that give birth to small litters, which they are unable to protect as efficiently as predatory animals can, must give birth to young who are in a fairly mature state. A long gestation period serves to allow for such maturation.

The elephant, which has a gestation period of 515 to 670 days, is monotocous, having but one young at a birth. In the polytocous fallow deer, which has two or three young at a birth, the gestation period is 230 days, and in the seal, which produces only a single pup at a birth, the gestation period varies from 245 to 350 days. Predatory animals, by contrast, are very efficient in protecting their young and have a short gestation period. Their litters may vary from three upward; the size of the young may be small at birth, and the young may be born in a somewhat immature state. The lion, for example, which generally has a litter of three pups, has a gestation period of 105 days. Man has a gestation period of 266½ days, which is distinctly in the class of long gestation periods. Since this is so, what can be the explanation for man's birth in so extremely immature a state? Quite clearly the human infant arrives in the world years before he becomes ready to take it on for himself. How has this come about?

The hypothesis proposed here is that man is born as immaturely as he is because—owing to the great increase in the size of his brain and consequently of his head—if he weren't born when he is, he wouldn't be born at all. As a result of discoveries made during the last forty years, it now seems probable that during the early evolution of man several important changes occurred simultaneously. In adaptation to the novel changes presented by the translation from a forest environment to the open plains—associated with the development of a toolmaking, hunting economy, and the accompanying high premium placed upon the development of the erect bipedal gait—the brain grew larger while the pelvic outlet grew smaller. At birth the average volume of the brain is 350 cubic centimeters. Were that volume to increase only slightly, the head could not pass through the birth canal. As it is, in many cases the size of the baby's head constitutes a hazard to both baby and mother. The rate of growth of the brain is proceeding at such a rate that it cannot continue within the womb and must continue outside the womb. In other words, the survival of the fetus and mother requires the termination of gestation within the womb (uterogestation or interogestation) when the limit of head size compatible with birth has been reached, and long before maturation occurs.

Gestation, then, is not completed by the act of birth but is only translated from gestation within the womb to gestation outside the womb (exterogestation). Professor John Bostock of the University of Queensland, Australia, has suggested that the limit of exterogestation be set at the stage of development of effective locomotion on all fours,[1] a suggestion which has a good deal of merit. According to this hypothesis, man spends the first half of his gestation period within the womb (uterogestation) and the second half of it outside the womb (exterogestation).

It is of interest to note that the average duration of exterogestation—that is, the period from birth to the development of quadrupedal locomotion—lasts exactly the same time, on the average, as the period of uterogestation: 266½ days. In connection with this, it is also to be noted that, while the mother nurses her infant, pregnancy will tend to be delayed.

For the child to learn what he must acquire in order to function as an adequate human being, he must have a large brain. It is a striking fact that by the time the child has attained his third birthday, he has also virtually achieved the full adult size of the brain. The brain volume of the average three-year-old child is 1,250 cubic centimeters, while the brain volume of the average adult is 1,400 cubic centimeters. Significantly, the human brain more than doubles in size during its first year of development, attaining, on the average, a volume of 800 cubic centimeters. About two-thirds of the total growth of the brain is achieved by the end of the first year, and it will take an additional two years to accomplish the same amount of growth, that is, to 1,250 cubic centimeters. In its first year, the infant's brain

[1] J. Bostock, "Exterior Gestation, Primitive Sleep, Enuresis and Asthma: Study in Aetiology," *Med. J. Aust.*, Vol. 2 (Aug. 2, 1958), pp. 149–53; (August 9, 1958), pp. 185–88.

does more growing than it will ever do again in any one year.

It is important that most of the brain growth be accomplished during the first year, when the infant has so much to learn and do, for the first year of life requires a great deal of unobtrusive packing for a journey that will endure the rest of the traveler's life. To perform this packing successfully, his brain must be much larger than 350 cubic centimeters, but quite clearly he cannot wait until he has grown a brain of 800 cubic centimeters before being born. Hence, he must be born with the maximum-sized brain possible and do the rest of his brain growing after birth. Since the human fetus must be born when its brain has reached the limit of size compatible with its admission through the birth canal, such maturation or further development as other mammals complete before birth will in the human mammal have to be completed after birth. In other words, the gestation period will have to be extended beyond birth.

If this interpretation of the gestation period is sound, then it would follow that we are not at present meeting the needs of infants in anything approaching an adequate manner. Although it is customary to regard the gestation period as terminated at birth, I suggest that this is quite as erroneous a view as that which regards the life of the individual as beginning at birth. Birth is no more the beginning of the life of the individual than it is the end of gestation; it is merely the bridge between uterogestation, gestation within the womb, and exterogestation, gestation continued outside the womb. It may be calendrically useful to divide up these periods as we have traditionally done, but it would appear to be quite unbiological to do so. It is unbiological because by making such arbitrary divisions, we lose sight of the essential fact that the human infant is quite as immature at birth as is the little marsupial immaturely born into its mother's pouch, there to undergo its exterogestation until it is sufficiently matured. The human infant remains immature much longer than the infant kangaroo or opossum, but whereas the marsupial infant enjoys the protection of its mother's pouch during its period of immaturity, the human infant is afforded no such natural advantage. This is all the more reason why the parental generation in such a species must clearly understand what the immaturity of its infants really means: with all the modifications initiated by the birth process, the baby is still continuing his gestation period, passing by means of birth from uterogestation to postnatal exterogestation. The biological unity, the symbiotic relationship, maintained by mother and conceptus throughout pregnancy does not cease at birth but becomes—indeed, is naturally designed to become—even more intensive and interoperative after birth than during uterogestation. It is not simply the infant who has a great need of continuing support from his mother after birth; the mother has, in a complementary manner, an equally great need to continue to support and to give succor to the child. Having given birth to her child, the mother's interest is deepened and reinforced in his welfare. Her whole organism has been readied to minister to his needs, to nurse him at her breast. In nursing, the infant ingests the beneficial colostrum, but nursing also confers benefits upon the mother. The psychophysiological benefits, which in the continuing symbiotic relationship mother and child reciprocally confer upon each other, are vitally important for their future development. The transfer of maternal antibodies to the baby through the milk in breast-feeding during the early exterogestative period, thus conferring immunities upon the infant, underscores both the biological reality and the importance of the symbiotic dependence of the infant upon the mother.

These facts are only slowly coming to be recognized in our highly sophisticated, mechanized Western world, a world in which breast-feeding is considered to be something that (as one expensively educated young woman remarked to me) "only animals do," and in which pediatricians practice who assure mothers that a bottle formula is every bit as good as, and even better than, breast-feeding. We live in the logical denouement of the Machine Age, when not only are things made by machine but human beings are turned out to be as machinelike as we can make them. We therefore see little wrong in dealing with others in a mechanical manner, since this is an age in which it is considered a mark of progress whenever anything that was formerly done by human beings is taken out of their hands and performed by machines. It is esteemed an advance when a bottle formula can be substituted for the product of the human breast, especially in the United States, and especially in a period when many women misguidedly strive to be as much like men as they believe they ought to be.

When mother and child most need each other, they are too often separated from each other, the one isolated in her room, the other banished to a crib in the nursery (so-called, presumably, because nursing is the one thing that is not done there). The separation begins from the moment of birth, so profound has our misunderstanding of the needs of human beings grown.

Perhaps the hypothesis of uterogestation and exterogestation proposed here may cause us to reconsider the meaning of the human infant's immaturity and dependency.[2]

2 See further: A. Montagu, *Prenatal Influences* (Springfield, Ill.: Charles C Thomas, 1962); *Life Before Birth* (New York: New American Library, 1966).

19. *Sex Order of Birth and Personality*

That siblings within a family interact with and act upon one another is obvious. The "only" child tends to develop a personality which, in many traits, is distinctively different from that of children who are influenced by the presence of siblings in their family. These things are fairly well understood. I should here like to draw attention to yet another fact which, it seems to me, has received too little attention. This is the relation of the sex order of birth of the siblings within a family to the personality development of each of them.

It scarcely requires pointing out that the quality of the relations between brothers and sisters differs from that which exists between siblings of the same sex. This holds true for all human societies. This observation, however, does not permit us to extrapolate to such generalizations as that boys who have been brought up in a family of male siblings are likely to be more masculine than those raised in a family of female siblings. This may or may not be so, but until the matter has been carefully investigated it were better to keep an open mind on the subject. It may be recalled how many biographers of Friedrich Nietzsche have sought to explain his personal gentleness as due to the fact that he was brought up almost exclusively by and in the society of his mother and sister. The imputed relation may be true in this case. The fact is, however, that most of us have known men who were reared almost exclusively by members of the opposite sex and these men were perfectly masculine in every way, and some extremely so. The relation is not a simple one. Many complex conditions and relations are involved, and these require detailed study.

Taken alone, sex order of birth tells us nothing about personality, but as a single factor in a total pattern, it is one that should be given careful consideration.

I have seen this factor operate in so pervasive a manner as to produce a complete alteration in the direction of development of a personality. The case I have in mind is that of two boys, in a family in which the firstborn was an only child for three years. At the end of his third year a brother was born, an event which produced an appreciable outcropping of jealous behavior. As George, the younger one, grew and began to make the affectionate advances which characterized his generous nature, they were consistently rejected by Basil, the older brother. George's whole personality was disturbed by Basil's behavior toward him, and out of sheer self-defense he was forced to learn to be almost, though not quite, as nasty as Basil. Had George inherited a brother of a kindlier disposition, George would have been as generous-natured as the obvious potentialities with which he was born allowed. As it was, his personality was considerably distorted by his older brother's behavior toward him.

George was in every way in competition with Basil for the affection of the world which had previously been Basil's exclusive oyster. Had George been born a girl, it is likely that Basil's response would have been different. A girl would not have found such a strong competitor, at least insofar as a member of the opposite sex (in our culture) competes on different terms. When, indeed, a sister, Elizabeth, was born to them when Basil was seven and George four years, both immediately became utterly devoted to her and have continued to be so to the present time. Elizabeth, an unusually attractive and gentle child, has been markedly affected by the rivalry behavior of her brothers and has adopted many of their traits. In another family in which the sexes happen to be exactly the reverse, the identical patterns of behavior have been observed.

It is clear that each of these children would have developed as very different personalities from what they became had they been only children. Basil would have made an ideal only child. When his siblings are away, he is as happy and delightful a child as can be imagined; the moment his brother enters the room the change that comes over him is striking. He becomes aggressive, tense, and fractious. Not so when his sister appears, though it is quite evident that he would rather share his parents' undivided attention.

It is of interest to note that Basil's parents have always permitted their children the free expression of hostility toward themselves. Such expressions are usually discussed for what they are worth, reasonably and sympathetically, with the children. Hate and aggressive responses among the children are not summarily suppressed by the parents. The attempt has been made to handle them judiciously; therefore, less tendency exists for the displacement of aggression toward the siblings from this source than is usually the case. Naturally the personalities of the parents have played a significant part in influencing those of the children, as have the differences in techniques by which the children have been reared. Allowing for these and all other factors, the important fact remains that the sex order of birth in which the children stand to one another is a relationship of some importance in the development of the personality which would bear further investigation.

Another matter to which I should like to draw attention is the personality of a firstborn. Over the course of the years many parents have commented to me upon the rather unfortunate personality of their oldest child. The traits complained of are chiefly those of "selfishness." These children belong to the generations born after 1920, with a modal distribution around the 1930's.

It may be that the experimental child-rearing theories which flourished in those years are in part responsible, or it may be that the tendency is to "spoil" the first child. In any event, most of the mothers of these children have independently expressed themselves in words which, in effect, amount to saying that "the first child is a mistake!" By the time the second child is born, they generally feel that they have learned enough to avoid committing the mistakes of which they were guilty with the first. By the third child they really feel sound and sane about the whole process of helping a baby grow into a human being.

The firstborn does seem to take rather a beating. For a year or more he is emperor of the universe. Everything exists to cater to his needs. He is loved by and learns to love those who satisfy his basic needs. Then more or less abruptly this halcyon existence is terminated or at least considerably changed by the irruption into it of a brother or sister. The attention the first-born receives is no longer the same; at best he must share it with the usurper. Under such circumstances it is not surprising that the firstborn is often what parents frankly call "a mess"!

Since the above was written, I have come across the following passages in Freud's *Introductory Lectures on Psychoanalysis:*

> Forced into the second place by the birth of another child and for the first time almost entirely parted from the mother, the child finds it very hard to forgive her for this exclusion of him; feelings which in adults we should describe as profound embitterment are roused in him, and often become the ground-work of a lasting estrangement. . . . As these new brothers and sisters grow up the child's attitude to them undergoes the most important transformations. A boy may take his sister as love-object in place of his faithless mother; where there are several brothers to win the favour of a little sister hostile rivalry, of great importance in

after life, shows itself already in the nursery. A little girl takes an older brother as a substitute for the father who no longer treats her with the same tenderness as in her earliest years; or she takes a little sister as a substitute for the child that she vainly wished for from her father.

So much and a great deal more of a similar kind is shown by direct observation of children, and by consideration of clear memories of childhood, uninfluenced by any analysis. *Among other things you will infer from this that a child's position in the sequence of brothers and sisters is of very great significance for the course of his later life, a factor to be considered in every biography.*[1]

1 *Introductory Lectures on Psychoanalysis* (London, 1929), pp. 280–81. Italics mine.

20. *Embryology from Antiquity to the End of the Eighteenth Century*

Egypt

It is a remarkable fact that while the Egyptians practiced artificial incubation of bird eggs, possibly as far back as the dawn of the Old Kingdom about 3000 B.C., they have left no record which might suggest that they exhibited any interest, either observational or speculative, in the process of development from egg to chick. The history of human thought is replete with queer twists, but surely among the queerest must be the fact that from 5,000 to 3,500 years ago the Egyptians were in possession of a method of incubating eggs which was not successfully achieved in the West until the nineteenth century. This method is one of the greatest helps in the systematic study of embryology, yet the Egyptians seem to have had little or no knowledge of embryology, while the West hit upon the method of studying eggs in various stages of development long before any observer was able to incubate them.

Nevertheless, it seems difficult to believe that the Egyptians were entirely without knowledge of some of the prenatal processes of development, even though they have left no writings on that subject. From those medical writings of theirs which have come down to us, such as the veterinary and gynecological papyri from Kahun (Middle Kingdom, 2160–1788 B.C.), it seems certain that whatever embryological knowledge the ancient Egyptians possessed must have been extremely crude, for their medicine and surgery was quite rudimentary.

It is more than passing strange that a people who were masters of a relatively highly developed mathematics and astronomy, who had replaced stone with bronze, who had made bricks, pottery, glass, and leather, who perfected the art of embalming to a degree which has never been surpassed, and who erected monuments which amaze the modern engineer should have been so unknowledgeable in developmental and gross anatomy, as well as in medicine itself.

Some embryological knowledge there was, and evidence of this we have from the fourteenth century B.C., in a hymn to the sun god Aton, written by the "heretic king" Amenophis IV (Akhnaton) and translated 3,300 years later by James H. Breasted:

> Creator of the germ in woman,
> Maker of seed in man,
> Giving life to the son in the body of his mother,
> Soothing him that he may not weep,
> Nurse (even) in the womb.
> Giver of breath to animate everyone that he maketh
> When he cometh forth from the womb on the day of his birth.
> Thou openest his mouth in speech,
> Thou suppliest his necessity.
> When the fledgling in the egg chirps in the shell
> Thou givest him breath therein to preserve him alive.
> When thou has brought him together
> To the point of bursting out of the egg,
> He cometh forth from the egg
> To chirp with all his might.
> He goeth about on his two feet
> When he hath come forth therefrom.

In this hymn the belief is clearly expressed that the germ exists in woman and the seed in man, and that through them Aton gives life to the child. Furthermore, that the soul (breath) is given to the fledgling when within the egg it chirps. Although it is not possible for a chick to chirp while still within the egg, evidently Akhnaton was familiar with the behavior of chicks as they pecked their way out of the shell and erroneously assumed that they chirped even before the shell was broken.

The important point to note here is that while the soul is given to man on the day of his birth, it is given to the chick while it is still in the shell "therein to preserve him alive." Here we have the first reference to what in later times became known as theological embryology, making possible a definite position on the moral status of abortion. The Egyptian soul doctrine must have been quite old, since the evidence is clear that from the earliest times the induction of abortion was severely punished.

The Egyptians appear to have believed that it was through the placenta that the soul was breathed into man; in any event, the placenta was supposed to be the seat of the external soul.

India

Among the oldest existing writings which contain statements referring to the prenatal development of man is the *Bhagavad-Gita,* the ancient Indian book of wisdom in the eighth century B.C. This work, written in Sanskrit, indicates that Indian embryology had achieved a relatively high level of development at an early age. For example, structures such as the amnion are referred to in this work, and various stages of fetal development are discussed.

In the *Khandogya-Upanishad* (seventh to eighth century B.C.?) the origin of living things is divided into three classes: "that which springs from an egg [oviparous], that which springs from a living being [viviparous], and that which springs from a germ."

In the *Ayur-Veda* (sixth to seventh century B.C.) the factors entering into the formation of the fetus are held to be (a) the father's semen, (b) the mother's blood (*śonita*), (c) the *átman,* or subtle body, (d) the *manas* or mind, united to a particular embryo by reason of its *karma.* The subtle body was composed of fire, earth, air, and water in the proper proportions.

The *Anugita Brahman* (fourth century B.C.) gives the origin of living things as fourfold:

> Those born from eggs, those born from germs, those born from perspiration, and those born from wombs. . . . Now there are the inferior beings and likewise those moving in the air. These should be understood to be born from eggs, so also all reptiles. Insects are said to be born from perspiration; and worms of the like description. This is said to be the second [mode of] birth, and inferior. Those beings, however, which are born after the lapse of some time, bursting through the earth, are said to be born from germs, O best of twice born! Beings of two feet or more than two feet, and those which move crookedly, are the beings born from wombs.

The two great Indian physicians of the sixth century, Susruta and Charaka, held that the blood entering into the production of the fetus was menstrual in origin. This is a view held by many nonliterate peoples, and it was also held by Aristotle. Since the menstrual blood was regarded as the *materia prima* of the embryo, the Indians considered it a crime, and in many parts of India still do, for a girl to menstruate before going from her father's to her husband's house; hence the institution of child marriage.

In the *Garba-Upanishad* (fifth century B.C.), "The Secret Teachings of the Embryo," there is contained a remarkable account of the development of the embryo. The new being is present in the form of a nodule by the first night following intercourse; it is vesicular in form by the seventh day and nodal a fortnight after intercourse. In one month this node becomes attached to the uterus, the head appearing after two months, the feet in three, the tarsals, abdomen, and hips in four, the vertebral column in five, and the nose, eyes, and ears in six months. The soul was considered to enter the body in the seventh month.

The order of the development of the various parts of the body was a matter, however, of much speculation among Indian writers, and there appears to have been no common agreement upon it. Nevertheless, some of this speculation would seem to have been based on observation though apparently not of a very systematic kind.

Pre-Socratic Greece

The pre-Socratic writers of Greece appear to have had very definite opinions on embryology, some of which are worth a reference here. Empedocles of Acragas (c. 495–435 B.C.) believed that "the embryo derives its composition out of vessels that are four in number, two veins and two arteries, through which blood is brought to the embryo." Sinews Empedocles held to be formed from an equal mixture of earth and air; the nails are water congealed, and the bones are formed from a mixture of equal parts of water and earth. Sweat and tears are made up of four parts of fire to one of water. Empedocles considered the origin of twins and monsters, and insisted that the influence of the maternal imagination upon the embryo was so great that its formation could be interfered with and guided. The fetus begins to take form after the thirty-first day and is completed within forty-nine days.

Anaxagoras of Clazomenae (c. 500–428 B.C.) held that the fire inside the embryo set the parts in order as it developed, and that the head was the first to be formed in development. This view was supported by Alcmaeon of Croton (sixth century B.C.) and by Hippon of Samos, a Pythagorean, in the fifth century

B.C., but Diogenes of Apollonia, on the other hand, asserted at about the same time that a mass of flesh was first formed and that the bones and nerves were differentiated later.

Diogenes maintained that the placenta is the organ of fetal nutrition and held that the male embryo was formed in four months but that the female embryo was formed in five months. Heat was the essential principle in the generation of little animals out of slime, and he compared this with the heat of the uterus in which the fetus is bred, it taking on life by drawing cold into the lungs as soon as it leaves the womb.

An idea which has persisted right into the second half of the twentieth century after Christ was put forward by Parmenides in the fifth century B.C., namely, that there is a connection between male embryos and the right side of the body and between female embryos and the left side of the body.

Democritus (born *c.* 460 B.C.) and Epicurus (born *c.* 342 B.C.) believed that the embryo obtained its nutrition by mouth, and that this explained the "nuzzling" with the mouth of the newborn infant. Alcmaeon affirmed, however, that the fetus fed with its whole body, taking nourishment in the manner of a sponge.

Hippocrates

It is with Hippocrates (*c.* 460–377 B.C.) that we arrive at a detailed embryological knowledge which is largely based on observation. In three books, *Regimen, On Generation,* and *On the Nature of the Infant,* his canon of embryology is set out.

The two main constituents of all natural bodies are fire and water. Each of these is made up of three primary nonseparable natures: heat, dryness, and moisture; and each has the power of attracting its like. Life consists in moisture's being dried up by fire and fire's being wetted by moisture alternately.

The theory of the formation of the embryo is set out in Section 9 of the *Regimen:*

Whatever may be the sex, which chance gives to the embryo, it is set in motion, being humid, by fire, and thus it extracts its nourishment from the food and breath introduced into the mother. First of all, this attraction is the same throughout because the body is porous but by the motion and fire it dries up and solidifies, as it solidifies, a dense outer crust is formed, and then the fire inside cannot any more draw in sufficient nourishment and does not expel the air because of the density of the surrounding surface. It therefore consumes the interior humidity. In this way parts naturally solid being up to a point hard and dry are not consumed to feed the fire but fortify and condense themselves the more the humidity disappears—these are called bones and nerves. The fire burns up the mixed humidity and forwards development towards the natural disposition of the body in this manner; through the solid and dry parts it cannot make permanent channels but it can do so through the soft, wet parts, for these are all nourishment to it. There is also in these parts a certain dryness which the fire does not consume, and they become compacted one to another. Therefore the most interior fire, being closed round on all sides, becomes the most abundant and makes the most canals for itself (for that was the wettest part) and that is called the belly. Issuing out from thence, and finding no nourishment outside, it makes the air pipes and those for conducting and distributing food. As for the enclosed fire, it makes three circulations in the body and what were the most humid parts become the *venae cavae*. In the intermediate part the remainder of the water contracts and hardens forming the flesh.

This is an extremely ingenious attempt at causal explanation in mechanistic terms, and the reference to the drying up of the embryo during development suggests an acquaintance with the facts, for the water content of the chick drops markedly from the fifth to the fourteenth day.

In Section 26 is contained a foreshadowing of the eighteenth-century doctrine of preformationism.

Everything in the embryo is formed simultaneously. All the limbs separate themselves at the same time and so grow, none comes before or after the other, but those which are naturally bigger appear before the smaller, without being formed earlier. Not all embryos form themselves in an equal time but some earlier and some later according to whether they meet with fire and water, some have everything visible in 40 days, others in 2 months, 3 or 4. They also become visible at various times and show themselves to the light having the blend (of fire and water) which they always will have.

In the treatise *On Generation,* the difference between the male and female seed is discussed and the latter identified with the vaginal secretion. In Section 14 it is stated that the embryo is nourished by maternal blood which finds its way to the fetus and there coagulates to form the embryonic flesh. This connection is proven by the fact that during pregnancy the flow of menstrual blood ceases; therefore it must be used up on its way out. In Section 15 the umbilical cord is recognized as the organ through which the fetal respiration is carried on. In Section 17 development is described: "The flesh brought together by the breath grows and divides itself into members, like going to like, dense to dense, flabby to flabby, humid to humid. The bones harden, coagulated by the heat."

The beginnings of systematic embryology can clearly be traced to a distinctive passage in Section 20. The Hippocratic embryologist says:

Now I shall speak of the characters which I promised above to discuss and which show as clearly as human intelligence can to anyone who will examine these things that the seed is in a membrane, that the umbilicus occupies the middle of it, that it alternately draws the air through itself and then expels it, and that the members are attached to the umbilicus. In a word, all the constitution of the fetus as I have described it to you, you will find from one end to the other if you will use the following proof: take 20 eggs or more and give them 2 or 3 hours to incubate, then each day from the second onwards till the time of hatching, take out an egg, break it, and examine it. You will find everything as I say in so far as a bird can resemble a man. He who has not made these observations before will be amazed to find an umbilicus in a bird's egg. But these things are so, and this is what I intended to say about them.

Quite as remarkable is the following discussion of the phenomenon of birth, which occurs in Section 30:

I say that it is the lack of food which leads to birth, unless any violence has been done; the proof of which is this: —the bird is formed thus from the yolk of the egg, the egg gets hot under the sitting hen and that which is inside is put into movement. Heated, that which is inside begins to have breath, and draws by counter-attraction another cold breath coming from the outside air and traversing the egg, for the egg is soft enough to allow a sufficient quantity of respiration to penetrate to the contents. The bird grows inside the egg and articulates itself exactly like the child as I have previously described. It comes from the yolk but it has its food from, and growth in, the white. To convince ourselves of this it is only necessary to observe it attentively. When there is no more food for the young one in the egg and it has nothing on which to live, it makes violent movements, searches for food, and breaks the membranes. The mother, perceiving that the embryo is vigorously moving, smashes the shell. This occurs after 20 days. It is evident that this is how things happen, for when the mother breaks the shell there is only an insignificant quantity of liquid in it. All has been consumed by the fetus. In just the same way, when the child has grown big and the mother cannot continue to provide him with enough nourishment, he becomes agitated, breaks through the membranes and incontinently passes out into the external world free from any bonds. In the same way among beasts and savage animals birth occurs at a time fixed for each species without overshooting it, for necessarily in each case there must be a point at which intrauterine nourishment will become inadequate. Those which have least food for the fetus come quickest to birth and *vice versa*. That is all that I had to say upon this subject.

With all its errors, this represents a brilliant piece of ratiocination. It is of interest to note that modern research tends to confirm this Hippocratic theory of the cause of birth; the modern findings show that there is a failure of the placenta toward the end of intrauterine life with an associated series of adaptive reactions on the part of the fetus, such as increased blood cell production and blood volume, reactions possibly brought about by a relative anoxemia caused by the placental inefficiency.

Aristotle

During the last three-quarters of the fourth century B.C., Aristotle composed five books which contained a considerable amount of embryological data: *The History of Animals, The Parts of Animals, On Respiration, On the Motion of Animals,* and *On the Generation of Animals.* The last of these is essentially an embryological treatise and exhibits the clearest evidence that Aristotle not only examined the eggs of birds at various stages of development but also that he examined the embryos of many animals. It is highly probable that he was acquainted with the early human fetus and possibly the late embryo.

The first of the five books, *On Generation,* discusses in considerable detail the basic phenomena of sex, its nature and character. There is an important refutation of the older and widely held view that the semen takes its origin from all the parts of the body in order that the characteristics of the parent be reproduced in the offspring. Semen is regarded as a true secretion and is held to supply the "form" to the embryo out of the menstrual blood supplied by the mother. The mother is not regarded as contributing any seed, and the male seed is regarded as determining nothing but the form.

Book II contains an embryological classification of animals and a brilliant discussion of epigenesis and preformation. Book III is concerned with comparative embryology, and Book IV brings together a host of minor embryological observations.

Aristotle's observations on the part played by the female in the generation of the fetus stands in striking contrast to the views which appear to have been widely held but a century earlier in Greece. These are illustrated in a famous passage in the *Eumenides* of Aeschylus, in which Apollo, defending Orestes from the charge of matricide, says:

> She who is called the mother of the child
> Is not its parent, but nurse of seed
> Implanted in begetting. He that sows
> Is author of the shoot, which she, if Heaven
> Prevent not, keeps as in a garden-ground
> In proof whereof (Apollo exclaims), to show that fatherhood
> May be without the mother, I appeal
> To Pallas, daughter of Olympian Zeus,
> In present witness here. Behold a plant
> Not moulded in the darkness of the womb,
> Yet nobler than all the scions of Heaven's stock.

Needham has pointed out that there is evidence that this doctrine was of Egyptian origin, for Diodorus Siculus says, "The Egyptians hold the father alone to be the author of generation, and the mother only to provide the nidus and nourishment for the fetus." The widespread denial of physiological maternity in early times has been traced by a number of investigators (Hartland, Cook, Vaughan), and it very probably antedates the earliest Egyptian beliefs. Aristotle says:

> When the material secreted by the female in the uterus has been fixed by the semen of the male (this acts in the same way as rennet acts upon milk, for rennet is a kind of milk containing vital heat, which brings into one mass and fixes the similar material, and the relation of the semen to the catamenia is the same, milk and the catamenia being of the same nature), when, I say, the more solid part comes together, the liquid is separated off from it, and as the earthy parts solidify membranes form all round it; this is both a necessary result and for a final cause, the

former because the surface of the mass must solidify on heating as well as on cooling, the latter because the foetus must not be in a liquid but separated from it.

The comparison of the formation of the embryo to the clotting of milk into curd occurs also in Susruta and in later Indian writers. This raises the interesting question of the direction in which this idea may have been diffused. It will be recalled that the notion occurs also in the Old Testament. Job (475 B.C.) asks, "Hast thou not poured me out as milk, and curdled me like cheese?" (10:10).

The Aristotelian concept of coagulation occurs also in the Wisdom of Solomon (150–50 B.C.), one of the Apocryphal books, where we read, "And in the womb of a mother was I molded into flesh in the time of ten months, being compacted in blood of the seed of man and pleasure that came with sleep" (7:1–2).

Embryonic growth is described by Aristotle as follows:

> The homogeneous parts (tissues) are formed by heat and cold, for some are put together and solidified by the one and some by the other.... The nutriment oozes through the blood-vessels and the passage in each of the parts, like water in unbaked pottery, and thus is formed the flesh or its analogues, being solidified by cold, which is why it is dissolved by fire. But all the particles given off which are too earthy; having but little moisture and heat, cool as the moisture evaporates along with the heat, so they become hard and earthy in character, as nails, horns, hoofs, and beaks, and therefore they are softened by fire but none of them is melted by it, while some of them, as egg-shells, are soluble in liquids. The sinews and bones are formed by the internal heat as the moisture dries, and hence the bones are insoluble by fire like pottery, for like it they have been as it were baked in an oven by the heat in the process of development.... The skin, again, is formed by the drying of the flesh, like the scum upon boiled substances; it is so formed not only because it is upon the outside, but also because what is glutinous, being unable to evaporate, remains on the surface.

These excerpts will serve to convey some idea of Aristotle's work as an embryologist; they represent but a minute fraction of that work, but they are representative of his contributions. For twenty centuries Aristotle's embryological concepts held the field, and as Needham says, "Embryology from the third century B.C. to the seventeenth century A.D. is meaningless unless it is studied in the light of Aristotle."

The Hellenistic Age

In the philosophies of the Stoics and Epicureans, embryological speculations are not wanting, but these are, in general, of little importance. The Epicureans believed that both male and female supplied seed in generation, and the Stoics looked upon the fetus as having the same relation to the womb as a fruit does to the tree which bears it.

Diocles of Carystus (350 B.C.) described the cotyledonous placenta, the *punctum saliens*, the character of human embryos at the twenty-seventh and fortieth days, and dissected the wombs of mules.

Herophilus of Chalcedon and Erasistratus of Chios, both of whom lived in the third century B.C., made several contributions to embryology. Herophilus described the ovaries and Fallopian tubes, and Erasistratus, so we surmise from references to his lost writings, discussed the growth of the embryo.

The Alexandrian school, of which Herophilus and Erasistratus were members, has its importance in the history of embryology in that it was through its agency that Greek medical and biological knowledge was introduced into Rome.

The most notable of Roman writers on embryology was Soranus, who lived in Rome from A.D. 30 to some twenty years before the birth of Galen. There is, however, nothing original in him, although he was widely quoted until the Middle Ages.

Galen of Pergamos (second century) wrote a treatise, *On the Formation of the Foetus,* in which he described the allantois, amnion, placenta, and membranes with considerable accuracy.

In his *On the Natural Faculties, Commentary on Hippocrates, On the Causes of Symptoms,* and *On the Use of Parts* are also included many interesting embryological statements which may be referred to here. Galen held embryonic life to consist of four types: (1) an unformed seminal stage, (2) a stage in which the *tria principia,* the heart, liver, and brain (a concept which occurs here for the first time), are engendered, (3) a stage when all the other parts are mapped out, and (4) a stage when all other parts have become clearly visible. As these stages unfold, the embryo rises from the status of a plant to that of an animal.

The distinction of Galen emerges again and again in his accurate anatomical descriptions; as for example, when he describes the umbilical cord and the junction of its veins with the branches of the portal vein, and the umbilical with the iliac arteries, the foramen ovale, the ductus venosus, and the ductus arteriosis. Galen held that fetal respiration occurred through the umbilical cord and maintained that blood passed in the embryo from the heart to the lungs and not the other way about. While Galen repeated many of the views of earlier writers, it is clear that he did make an attempt to use his own judgment independently; but on the whole he cannot be said to have advanced embryological knowledge, in spite of his excellent descriptions, much further than he found it.

Embryology from Galen to the Renaissance

The theological embryology of the patristic writers and the views of the Jewish Talmudic commentators need not detain us here, nor need those of the similarly speculative Arabian writers. The few bare and barren references to the subject added nothing to embryological knowledge, and so we may pass directly to the work of several medieval writers.

Albertus Magnus

Albertus Magnus of Cologne (1206–1280), a Dominican friar and for a time Bishop of Regensburg, published a treatise in twenty-six books entitled *De animalibus,* in which, basing his views largely on those of Aristotle, he intermixes a number of traditional and original observations. Thus, he describes the pulsating drop of blood in the chick egg on the third day and identifies it with the heart in systole and diastole; he also observes that at first the development of the chick proceeds rapidly and that later it proceeds more slowly. His account of the relationship between yolk and embryo in fishes represents a definite improvement upon Aristotle.

It appears probable from Albert's descriptions that he not only opened hen and fish eggs at different stages of development but also dissected them. Albert was not a systematic writer, and he was still very much a scholastic; nevertheless he was something of a believer in observation, in *anathomyam,* investigation, and as such he strikes a new note. His contribution to embryology is chiefly that of a compiler and commentator who helped lay the foundations for further advance.

As a commentary on human folly, it is of interest to note that an English translation of the epitome of Albert's writings on generation (*De secretis mulierum*), under the title *Aristotle's Masterpiece,* still sells thousands of copies in England every year. I presume that it is also available in the United States. In Western Europe it has long been the main source of most of the sexual and embryological knowledge of the working class populations.

The Scholastic Period

The theological embryology of Albert's favorite disciple, Thomas Aquinas (1227–1274), with its preoccupation in developing the idea of a vegetative soul making way for a sensitive soul which is finally replaced by a rational soul provided directly by God is typical of scholastic embryology—Aristotelianism dramatically reconciled with Christian theology.

Leonardo da Vinci

Leonardo da Vinci (1452–1519), that supreme genius, was intensely interested in the embryonic development of mammals and birds. Unfortunately, his drawings and observations on this subject were not published until several centuries after his death, yet Needham says of him: "If Aristotle is the father of embryology regarded as a branch of natural history, Leonardo is the father of embryology regarded as an exact science." How true this judgment is may be judged from the following excerpts, which are to be found in Leonardo's *Quaderni d'Anatomia.*

> You should make the liver in the embryo differing from that in a man, that is, with the right and left parts equal.
>
> But you should make first the anatomy of the hatched eggs.
>
> Say how at four months the child is half the length and so is one-eighth the weight that it will be at birth.
>
> Your order shall commence with the formation of the child in the womb, saying which part of it is formed first and so on in succession, placing its parts according to the times of pregnancy until the birth, and how it is nourished, learning in part from the eggs which eggs make.
>
> Why the heart does not beat nor the lung breathe during the time that the child is in the womb which is filled with water; for if it should draw a breath it would instantly be drowned. But the breathing and the beating of its mother's heart works in the life of the child which is joined to her by means of the umbilical cord as it works in the other members.
>
> The child grows daily far more when in the body of its mother than when it is outside of the body and this teaches us why in the first year when it finds itself outside the body of the mother, or, rather, in the first 9 months, it does not double the size of the 9 months when it found itself within the mother's body. Nor in 18 months has it doubled the size it was 9 months after it was born, and thus in every nine months diminishing the quantity of such increase till it has come to its greatest height.

Leonardo recognized the amnion and allantois but knew them only from his dissection of lower mammals. In his beautiful drawing of the fetus within the uterus, it is of interest to observe that cotyledons of the ungulate type are represented on the wall of the uterus, while the discoidal placenta is entirely overlooked. He was aware that at birth each cotyledon divides, a part remaining connected with the uterus and part adhering to the chorion, and he gives figures showing the separation.

It is a tragedy that Leonardo's works remained for so long unpublished, for had they been available there can be little doubt of the great influence in the right direction which they would have exerted.

The Renaissance

One of the great, but little-known, figures of the Renaissance was the anatomist Jacopo Berengario da Carpi (1470–1550), professor of surgery at Bologna and, incidentally, Benvenuto Cellini's physician. In his *Commentario ... super anatomia Mundini,* published at Bologna in 1522, he strongly urged the study of the fetus because, he held, its organs are simpler than those of the adult and one may study in the fetus those transitional stages of development which one may see only as vestiges in the fully developed organism.

Andreas Vesalius (1514–1564), the father of modern anatomy, in his great work, *De humani corporis fabrica,* published in 1543, and in the second edition thereof published in 1555, included many original observations on embryology. He dissected the fetuses of several mammals, but particularly that of the dog, and it is of interest to note that he himself committed the very fault of which he accused Galen, namely, of sometimes attributing to man structures which he had observed only in lower animals.

Vesalius described the annular placenta of the dog, under the impression that it was the chorion, and took the chorion to be the allantois. He observed and correctly described the vernix caseosa, and in the second edition of the *Fabrica,* for the first time in the literature, clearly differentiates the discoidal placenta of man, the annular placenta of the dog, and the cotyledonous placenta of ruminants. These are illustrated in his figures, and they are of further interest because they represent the first illustrations of the comparative anatomy of the placenta.

Vesalius initiated studies in the comparative anatomy of the ruminant and human uterus in order to clear up the rather confused Galenic conception of the term "cotyledon." By means of comparative dissections, Vesalius was able to show that true cotyledons are found only in ruminants.

Realdus Columbus (1516–1559) literally repeated the embryology of Vesalius, except that he saw the sausage-shaped allantois in animals other than man and corrected Vesalius on this point. But his principal contribution is his introduction of the term "placenta" to describe the "cakelike" placenta in man, which he then proceeded to identify with the chorion.

Gabriel Faloppius (1523–1562), the successor of Vesalius in the chair of anatomy at Padua, in his *Observationes Anatomicae,* published at Paris in 1562, observed that there is only a single umbilical vein in man but two in the sheep, goat, and ox. He stated that the human fetus does not have an allantois, that this membrane is found only in ruminants. He discussed the confusion of ancient writers concerning cotyledons, and with Vesalius erroneously concluded that the pregnant ruminant uterus possessed such structures.

Julius Caesar Arantius (1530–1589), in his little treatise *De Formato Foetu,* maintained that the fetal and maternal circulations are quite separate and that the placenta is an organ which serves to purify the blood—that it is, in fact, a uterine liver—and that the human urachus is not a patent canal but a ligament which attaches the neck of the bladder to the peritoneum. He also agreed with Faloppius that the human fetus lacks an allantois.

These men were primarily interested in fetal anatomy rather than in developmental anatomy or embryology. It was Volcher Coiter who took up the subject where they had left off.

Volcher Coiter (1534–1600?), the pupil of Faloppius and Arantius, in his work as an embryologist most clearly exhibited the character of the Renaissance investigator who had freed himself from the bias of scholasticism. It was in May, 1564, as Adelmann says, that Coiter, probably for the first time since Aristotle, examined the developing chick on each successive day of incubation.

In his book *Externarum et internarum principalium humani corporis partium tabulae,* published at Nuremberg in 1572, Coiter first gave an excellent account of the anatomy of the reproductive tract in the hen, though he failed to understand the function of the ovary and was unclear on such matters as the role of the oviduct in the formation of the egg.

Coiter's account of the development of the chick must always rank as one of the great landmarks in the history of science. It is extraordinarily accurate and far surpasses the work of Aristotle. He was the first to describe the egg tooth in a twelve-day-old embryo, and he gave an admirable account of the yolk sac and its eventual inclusion within the abdominal cavity. His recognition of the fact that the contraction of the amnion plays a part in this process represents an astonishing piece of scientific induction.

Ulysses Aldrovandus (1522–1605), the teacher of Coiter, who suggested to the latter his studies on chicks, was the first to present illustrations of the reproductive tract of the hen in his *Ornithologia,* published at Bologna in 1600. Aldrovandus described the chief features of the oviduct and improved on Coiter by describing the infundibulum and its communication with the body cavity. His day-by-day account of the development of the chick is inferior to that of Coiter; it is accompanied by a single illustration, the first of its kind, of a chick about to hatch.

Embryology in the Seventeenth Century

The modern science of development, embryology, takes its origin in the seventeenth century, that heroic age of science which saw the birth and rise of the experimental method. It is to the spirit of the new age of science and the meticulous attention to observation which the experimental method encouraged that the embryology of the seventeenth century owed its ascendancy above all the centuries which preceded it. This was likewise true for all the natural and physical sciences.

So far as embryology is concerned, the difference in viewpoint was fundamental. Whereas before the seventeenth century, development was viewed as a series of changing shapes occurring in more or less orderly succession, as a series of static conditions, the seventeenth century began to manifest an interest in the nature of these conditions and to inquire into the nature of the causes which produced them.

The first considerable figure in the history of embryology in this century is Jerome Fabricius of Aquapendente (1533–1619), professor of anatomy at Padua for more than fifty years, pupil of Faloppius, and later teacher of William Harvey. Although Fabricius' embryological works were published in the seventeenth century, they belong in spirit to the preceding century, and indeed there is evidence that the first published of them had already been completed before the last decade of the sixteenth century, namely, *De formato foetu,* published at Padua in 1604 or 1606. Fabricius' second work on embryology, *De formatione ovi et pulli* (Padua, 1621), was published two years after his death. In the logical order of Fabricius' scheme the latter work precedes the former.

Fabricius was, like others before and after him, a mixture of indifferent observer and great respecter of authority, and this conflicting mixture is reflected throughout his work. In his *De formatione ovi et pulli,* Fabricius perpetuated many errors and perpetrated a number of his own, and in so doing he undoubt-edly served to retard the development of embryology quite as much as he advanced it. His original observations and admi-rable illustrations served his readers well, and it is for these that he should be remembered. In the first part of the book Fabricius deals with the structure, action, and functions of the uterus; in the second part he deals in like manner with the egg. The beau-tiful illustrations which accompany Fabricius' *De formatione ovi et pulli* are far more accurate and show many more details than are recognized either in the text or in the legends. The excellent illustrations which accompany *De formato foetu*, how-ever, do contain full explanations in the colored plates which were issued with some copies, so that we may perhaps suppose, as suggested by Adelmann, that Fabricius, in his text, was more concerned with general principles than with factual details. The latter were left for the descriptive matter which was to accom-pany the colored plates; his death before the publication of *De formatione ovi et pulli* prevented this. In this work Fabri-cius gave the best account written up to this time of the repro-ductive tract of the hen, and in it for the first time established the role played by the ovary and oviduct in the formation of the hen's egg. His illustrations of the daily progress of the chick's development were remarkable for both detail and ac-curacy.

In *De formato foetu* he first clearly differentiated the diffuse placenta from other types and introduced a classification which agrees very closely with modern conceptions of placental mor-phology and physiology, and as Adelmann says, he "gave us a set of illustrations of the comparative anatomy of the placenta unique in his day and not without value in ours. Further, he coined a number of new terms and thus put useful tools of expression into the hands of his followers. And perhaps most important of all, he handed the torch to a brilliant student, William Harvey, who took it up and carried it a little further along the way."

William Harvey

In 1651 William Harvey (1578–1657) was persuaded to publish his observations, made over the course of many years, on the generation of animals. First issued in Latin as *De generatione animalium,* an English translation appeared in 1653. Harvey's original contributions to embryology were many. He was the first to demonstrate that the chalazae had no connection whatsoever with the seed of the cock, as most previous writers had asserted, and that it did not provide the material out of which the embryo was formed, but that the cicatricula was the point of origin of the embryo, "the first Principle of the Egge." Harvey's account of the development of the embryo in the egg remains, as Needham says, to this day one of the most accurate. His description of the beginning heart, that "capering bloody point," is brilliant, though, because he lacked a microscope, he erred in saying that the heart does not pulsate before the appearance of blood. It was Malpighi's later correction of this error which may be said to have started the great discussion of preformation versus epigenesis. Harvey argued in favor of epigenesis, the view which holds, in Harvey's words, "that one thing is made out of another," that is, by the differentiation of tissues. Harvey thus forever disposed of the doctrine of metamorphosis in the following words:

> The perfect animals, which have blood, are made by Epigenesis, or super-addition of parts, and do grow, and attain their just future or *akun* after they are born. . . . An animal produced by Epigenesis, attracts, prepares, concocts, and applies, the Matter at the same time, and is at the same time formed, and augmented. . . . Wherefore Fabricius did erroneously seek after the matter of the chicken (as it were some distinct part of the egg which went to the imbodying of the chicken) as though the generation of the chicken were effected by a Metamorphosis, or transfiguration of some collected lump or mass, and that all the parts of the body, at least the Principall parts, were wrought off at a heat or (as

himselfe speaks) did arise and were corporated out of the same Matter.

Yet Harvey was largely an Aristotelian in many of his embryological views, and he raised for discussion many unprofitable questions. Nevertheless his positive contributions far outweighed his metaphysical Aristotelianism, and had he written nothing but this work his claim on the attention of posterity would undoubtedly remain secure.

As physician to Charles I, Harvey enjoyed many opportunities for the dissection of does and hinds from the king's forest at Hampton Court. By this means he was able to obtain a number of embryos which he carefully described and compared with the embryos of birds and other creatures. His doctrine *omne vivum ex ovo* represented an important advance and was presented some seventeen years before Francesco Redi successfully challenged the doctrine of spontaneous generation.

Among other things, Harvey conclusively demonstrated the independence of the maternal and fetal circulations, and by demonstrating the unreality of the distinction, settled the problem of which part of the egg was nutritive and which formative.

Physical Embryology: Gassendi and Descartes

Pierre Gassendi's (1592–1655) *De generatione animalium et de animatione foetus,* published at Lyons in his *Opera Omnia* in 1658, and René Descartes' (1596–1650) treatise on the formation of the fetus in his *De homine liber,* Leyden, 1662, are notable for the fact that they attempted to derive embryology from physical and geometrical laws. They were not only ahead of their time but also ahead of themselves; their generalizations might have been of value had there been a sufficient number of particular instances to support them. Their work, however, stimulated some interest, and its modern descendant is represented by physicochemical embryology.

The year 1661 is notable, for in it was published, at Groningen, Deusingius' *Historia foetus extra uterum in abdomine geniti,* in which he describes a case of abdominal pregnancy.

Nicholas Stensen (1638–1686) made a very great, but virtually completely overlooked, contribution when he demonstrated the follicles in the ovaries of dogfish and stated that the "testis" of women ought to be regarded as the same organ as the "ovary" or "roe" of ovipara. This was published in his *Elementorum myologiae specimen,* issued at Florence in 1667.

It was Regner de Graaf (1641–1673) who, in 1672, gave a detailed description of the mammalian follicle, "the Graafian follicle." He erred, however, in thinking that the whole of the follicle was the ovum.

In 1668 Francesco Redi (1626–1698), by well-conceived experiments, proved that maggots do not arise spontaneously in rotting meat but are hatched from the eggs of flies. If the putrefying meat is protected with a thin cloth, maggots will not arise in it. This demonstration can hardly be said to have given a deathblow to the belief in spontaneous generation, for even Redi himself believed that intestinal worms and gallflies arose in this manner. In the eighteenth century such men as Buffon and Lamarck could still support the doctrine as efficiently as Aristotle had in the case of fleas and mosquitoes.

Marcello Malpighi and Preformationism

The founder of modern embryology is Marcello Malpighi (1628–1694), who, in his tractates *De ovo incubato* and *De formatione pulli in ovo,* published by the Royal Society at London in 1672, well and truly laid the foundations of the science. With the aid of the simple microscope he studied the development of the chick embryo during its first hours of incubation. For the first time he described the blastoderm, the neural groove, the optic vesicles, the somites, and the aortic arches.

It was in his study of the cicatricula that Malpighi went astray and gave the doctrine of preformationism—the simple unfolding of already preexisting structures—an apparently unquestionable experimental basis. He says that in the center of the cicatricula he perceived a saccule, in which:

> As in an amnion, when I held it up to the sunlight, I perceived the enclosed foetus, whose head, together with the stamina of the attached carina, clearly appeared. For the thin and clear texture of the amnion was frequently transparent, so that the imprisoned animal came into view. I often opened the follicle with the point of a needle in order that the imprisoned animal might come forth into the light; but without success, for they were so mucous and so tiny that they were all torn by a light touch. Therefore I declare that the stamina of the chick already exists in the egg, and it must be admitted that an earlier origin has been discovered, just as with the eggs of a plant.

John Mayow

John Mayow (1645–1679) published his remarkable tractate *De respiratione in utero et ovo* in 1674, and in this he made the first contribution to physiological embryology of any importance. By ingenious experimental means Mayow showed, to quote his own words, "that the blood of the embryo, conveyed by the umbilical arteries to the placenta or uterine carunculae, brings not only nutritious juice, but along with this a portion of nitro-aerial particles to the foetus for its support, so that it seems that the blood of the infant is impregnated with nitro-aerial particles by its circulation through the umbilical vessels quite in the same way as in the pulmonary vessels. And, therefore, I think that the placenta should no longer be called a uterine liver but rather a uterine lung."

The writer of these admirable sentences, and of much else that was admirable in the same work, died at the early age of thirty-four.

Antony van Leeuwenhoek

In November, 1677, Antony van Leeuwenhoek (1632–1723) communicated to the Royal Society a discovery made by a young

Leyden medical student, Johan Ham van Arnhem, and confirmed by himself: the existence of spermatozoa in man. This
communication was published in the *Philosophical Transactions* of the Royal Society of London under the title *Observationes de natis e semine genetali animalculis*. Leeuwenhoek's
statements were at first received with much incredulity, particularly his account of the very large numbers of "animalcula"
observed in a single ejaculate. He insisted upon the accuracy
of his observations and pointed out that seeds of plants occurred
in great numbers and that most of them were in fact lost, and
as early as 1683 he suggested that there might be but a single
point where a spermatozoon could enter the ovum and hence
that it might be necessary to have thousands present in order
that one would find it. In spite, however, of the fact that Anto-
nio Vallisnieri (1661–1730), Lazzaro Spallanzani (1729–1799),
and Robert Hooke (1635–1703) confirmed Leeuwenhoek's observations, many scientists continued to think of spermatozoa as
parasites until 1850. Leeuwenhoek believed that the future being arose from the spermatozoon and that the egg simply provided nourishment and powers of development. This theory he
tried to prove by pairing different-colored rabbits, and he found
confirmation of it when he discovered that a white female
paired with a gray male yields gray offspring. Had he continued
his experiments further, the extraordinary Leeuwenhoek might
have developed some interesting genetical ideas.

Finally, Leeuwenhoek was the first to explain the reproduction of ants, to describe their eggs, and to demonstrate that
what had previously been taken to be their eggs were really the
pupae of the insect.

In the present account of the history of embryology it has
been possible to deal only with the principal contributors to its
development. There were many others who served to advance
the science, and we may well conclude with the statement of one
of them, Edward Tyson (1650–1708), who in his *Phocaena, Or
the Anatomy of a Porpess* (London, 1680), the first separately

published monograph on the anatomy of any animal in the English language, formulated the following procedure:

> Lastly, *Embryotomia and the History of Generation.* These as they will require a great deal of Labour in the Research, so will they abundantly recompense the Pains by the great plenty they will afford of fruitful Observations. Nature viewed in her naked form, in the first organization of Animal Bodies, before she hath drawn over the veil of the flesh, and obscured her first lines by the succeeding varnish of her last hand, more freely displays herself, and suffers us to behold the disjoynted Parts of this admirable Machine, and how it is that in time she puts them all together: this certainly will be of the greatest consequence both for the knowing the structure and the uses of the Parts.

Embryology in the Eighteenth Century

The first work of any consequence on embryology to appear in the eighteenth century was Antoine Maître-Jan's (1650?–1730) *Observations sur la formation du poulet* (Paris, 1722). Incidentally, Maître-Jan was the first to recognize the true nature of cataract (1706). His embryological work was excellent and his technique superb. He hardened embryos in "distilled spirits of vinegar" in order better to dissect them. He was the first to demonstrate and figure the villosities on the interior of the yolk sac.

Martin Schurig's *Embryologia Historico-Medica* (Dresden-Leipzig, 1732) is notable as the first exhaustive review of all that had been written on embryology up to the end of the first quarter of the eighteenth century.

Hermann Boerhaave (1668–1738), through his widely studied *Elementa chemiae* (Leyden, 1732), created much interest in chemical embryology. Nevertheless his ingenious and accurate experiments failed to influence others to conduct research upon similar lines.

One of the most remarkable students of embryology of the eighteenth century was Georgius Erhardius Hamberger (1697–

1755), who in his *Physiologia medica* (Jena, 1751) published the first quantitative observations on the water content of the embryo and its growth rate. His values are very close to those obtained by modern investigators. He held some curious views on spermatozoa, saying that the tails of spermatozoa represented an extension of the vertebral column, and that only animals with tails possessed tailed spermatozoa!

Other investigators who made distinguished contributions to quantitative embryology in the first half of this century were J. B. Mazin in his *Conjecturae physico-medico-hydrostaticae de respiratione foetus* (Brixen, 1737) and *Tractatus medico-mechanica* (Brussels, 1742), Josephy Onymos in *De natura foetu* (Leyden, 1745), and J. C. Heffter in *De causis in crem. foetu* (Erfurt, 1745).

Albrecht von Haller (1708–1777), than whom no man was ever more deservedly called "great," among his numerous other brilliant contributions to knowledge made many important ones to embryology. These were published in Volumes 7 and 8 of his *Elementa physiologiae,* which appeared in 1766, and in his volume *Ad generationem* (Lausanne, 1767). Interestingly enough, Haller was once an epigenesist but became a confirmed preformationist following his discovery that the intestine and yolk sac are continuous. He confused the vitelline membrane with the yolk sac, assuming that therefore the differentiation of the cell layers could not take place and that epigenesis was impossible. Haller's work on the growth rate of the embryo and fetus is fundamental and has a remarkably modern ring, while his work on the growth of various organs and the development of the chick heart are superb. Haller studied the developing bones and concluded that the muscles drew out the various prominences to which they were attached and also bent and molded them. He recognized some of the early ossifactory centers and distinguished between endochondral and membranous ossification, and he measured, listed, and calculated the increments of growth of fetal bones.

Caspar Friedrich Wolff (1733–1794), a young member of the Russian Academy under Catherine the Great, was responsible for writing, at the age of twenty-six, the first thoroughgoing attack on preformationism. This was contained in his *Theoria generationis* (Halle, 1759), an ingenious speculative work which was widely read. But the work which gave the deathblow to the doctrine of preformationism was Wolff's experimentally based and armed *De formatione intestinorum praecipue,* published in 1768 and 1769 by the Academy of Sciences at St. Petersburg. This work was virtually entirely overlooked until it was published in 1821 in a German translation by Johann Friedrich Meckel (1781–1833). Since this work properly belongs to the nineteenth century, it cannot be further considered here, except to say that its influence during the second half of the century was considerable.

In 1749 appeared the earliest paper on the permeability of the placenta to pathological agents. This was W. Watson's "Some Accounts of the Foetus *in Utero* Being Differently Affected by the Small Pox," published in the *Philosophical Transactions* of the Royal Society. In 1755 Flemyng discussed deglutition of the amniotic fluid and concluded that the fetus derived some of its nutriment from the amniotic liquor. Experiments were performed on the transposition of the white of eggs from one to another egg host. Attempts to cross animals of different orders were unsuccessfully made, and much time was given to the controversial discussion of preformationism versus epigenesis. This controversy was far from barren in its results, for it stimulated investigations calculated to resolve the points at issue. Here Caspar Wolff made the fundamental contribution, but it was not until the next century that it, together with the work of others, triumphantly settled the case and gave the verdict for epigenesis. In general, it is interesting to observe that preformationism was the doctrine of the orthodox; epigenesis was the creed of the "advanced" thinkers of such men as Needham and Maupertuis. The Abbé John Tuberville Needham, in his *Observations nouvelles sur la Génération*, 1750, and Pierre de Maupertuis, in his *Vénus Physique*, 1746, boldly spoke out for epigenesis. Men like Buffon (1707–1788), who occupied an intermediate position, reconciling both views of the nature of embryogeny, also made their influence felt. Buffon's account of the development of the chick and of man, his views on the functions of the amniotic fluid and the umbilical cord, give him a very high place in the history of embryology.

In 1774 was published William Hunter's (1718–1783) great masterpiece, *The Anatomy of the Human Gravid Uterus Exhibited in Figures*. In addition to the fact that this work raised obstetrics to the plane of a science, in it Hunter conclusively proved the separateness of the fetal and maternal circulations.

Johann Friedrich Blumenbach (1752–1840), the father of physical anthropology, produced in 1789 a work entitled *Über den Bildungstrieb*, in which the Wolffian *vis essentialis* was elaborated into the *nisus formativus*, a morphogenetic force which Blumenbach conceived to be peculiar to living bodies, and which actively shaped the body. This view was essentially that of Wolff.

The history of embryology follows a pattern which has more or less characterized the development of every science. In the earliest period, speculation based on very incomplete observation is the rule; this is followed by closer attention to the observable material and then in turn by some attempt to set it out and interpret its meaning. In the absence of certain technical aids such as the microscope and hardening agents like alcohol, the limits of the development of the science of embryology were strictly determined. Until these two inventions were made, further progress was impossible. With their invention and development many new facts were discovered and the science greatly advanced. The history of embryology subsequent to the eighteenth century is to a large extent the story of the manner in which technical devices were increasingly applied to the mastery of problems which without their aid would have been insoluble. As a direct consequence, greater progress was made in the development of embryology in the nineteenth century than in all previous periods.

BIBLIOGRAPHY

Adelmann, H. B., *The Embryological Treatises of Hieronymus Fabricius of Aquapendente* (Ithaca, N.Y.: Cornell University Press, 1942).

Chaine, J., *Histoire de l'anatomie comparative* (Bordeaux: Daguerre, 1925).

Cole, F. J., *Early Theories of Sexual Generation* (Oxford: Oxford University Press, 1930).

Cook, S. A., Note to the 3d edition of Robertson Smith's *Religion of the Semites* (New York: Macmillan, 1927), Vol. I, p. 537.

Esser, A. M., "Moderne europäische und alt-indische Embryologie, eine Vergleichung," *Münchener medizinische Wochenschrift,* Jahrg. 72, S. 1643–45 (1925).

Hartland, E. S., *Primitive Paternity* (London: David Nutt, 1909), Vol. I, p. 309.

Meyer, A. W., *The Rise of Embryology* (Stanford University Press, 1939).

Montagu, M. F. Ashley, *Coming into Being Among the Australian Aborigines* (New York: Dutton, 1938).

Müller, M. F. (ed.), *The Sacred Books of the East* (Oxford: Clarendon, Press, 1879; 1882; 1886; 1900).

Needham, J., *A History of Embryology* (Cambridge: Cambridge University Press, 1934).

Webb, A., *Pathologica Indica* (Calcutta: Thacker, 1846).

Vaughan, A. C., *The Genesis of Human Offspring* (Smith College Classical Studies, No. 13, 1945).

21. *Physiological Paternity in Australia*

Ever since the publication in 1899 of Spencer and Gillen's *The Native Tribes of Central Australia,* the work in which it was first declared that there were aboriginal tribes in existence in Australia who possessed no knowledge whatsoever of the relationship between intercourse and pregnancy,[1] there has been a great deal of discussion concerning the nature of this ignorance and not a little controversy. The ground had long been prepared upon which such a discovery could fall with fruitful advantage by the writings of the evolutionists, whose views were given a syncretic summarization in this connection by Hartland in 1894 in the first volume of his *The Legend of Perseus,* in which the suggestion was put forward that "the world-wide-story-incident of Supernatural Birth" probably originated in a period when the physical relationship between father and child was imperfectly understood, or rather, not understood at all.[2] It remained for Spencer and Gillen to provide the proof that tribes exhibiting such a nescience of the facts of procreation actually existed in central Australia.

[1] B. Spencer and F. J. Gillen, *The Native Tribes of Central Australia* (London, 1899), pp. 122–25.
[2] E. S. Hartland, *The Legend of Perseus* (London, 1894), Vol. 1.

In 1903 W. E. Roth published the first independent confirmation of the existence of a similar nescience among the North Queensland tribes.[3]

In 1904 Spencer and Gillen published their observations on the northern tribes of central Australia among whom they found to exist a precisely similar nescience of the facts of procreation as they had first reported for the Central tribes.[4]

In September, 1905, J. G. Frazer published his now famous development of Spencer and Gillen's findings in this connection in the form of his theory of conceptional totemism.[5] Not quite two months later Andrew Lang launched his attack on both this theory and the findings of Spencer and Gillen.[6]

And from that day to this there has been an unceasing stream of writing devoted to this subject, reports of fieldworkers, discussions original and otherwise, and a great deal of expressing of doubts. I have calculated that during the first forty years of this century an average of about ten papers and books per annum, largely devoted to the discussion of what still remains the problem of the procreative beliefs of the Australian aborigines, regularly made their appearance, not to mention the numerous references to the subject in the more general sociological literature.

In the twenties the subject received a definite fillip as a result of the publication of Professor Malinowski's researches among the Trobriand Islanders.[7]

To read all this published material is enough to turn one's

3 W. E. Roth, *Superstition, Magic, and Medicine: North Queensland Ethnography* (Bulletin, Home Secretary's Department, No. 5, Brisbane, 1903).

4 B. Spencer and F. J. Gillen, *The Northern Tribes of Central Australia* (London, 1904), pp. 281–332.

5 J. G. Frazer, "Beginnings of Religion and Totemism among the Australian Aborigines," Pt. II (*Fortnightly Review*, Vol. 84, 1905, pp. 452–66).

6 A. Lang, *The Secret of the Totem* (London, 1905).

7 B. Malinowski, "Baloma: The Spirits of the Dead in the Trobriand Islands," *Journal, Royal Anthropological Institute*, Vol. 46 (1916), pp. 353–430; *Fatherhood in Primitive Psychology* (London, 1927); *The Sexual Life of Savages* (London, 1929).

hair gray, but if one is able to struggle through to the end what transpires is this:

By far the largest number of fieldworkers assert that the Australians are ignorant of the relationship between intercourse and childbirth.

Some fieldworkers state that while the tribes investigated by them have held the "mystical" beliefs of the Arunta type, yet they have also known that coitus is necessary before childbirth can occur.

The discussers of the evidence are of two kinds, critical and uncritical. One group of critical discussers asserts that the Australians may be ignorant of the relationship between intercourse and pregnancy today, though even this is doubtful, but granting that it is so, it seems highly probable that they were not always so ignorant and that their present ignorance is due to the repression or gradual obfuscation of knowledge which became incompatible with later developed spiritual beliefs; psychology, as Lang put it, obscuring physiology.

Another group of critical discussers asserts that there is no reason to believe that the presence nescience was ever preceded by a knowledge of the facts.

The uncritical discussers simply "naïvely" accept the statements of the early investigators that the nescience exists and is complete.

It is unfortunately quite impossible, without devoting a book to the subject,[8] to attempt to consider the merits either of the field reports or the discussions of them, but since Donald Thomson [9] has joined forces with those discussers who believe that the ignorance of physiological paternity is not primitive wherever found today, but is a condition resulting from the superimposition of certain animistic beliefs upon an older dogma,

[8] See Ashley Montagu, *Coming into Being Among the Australian Aborigines* (London: George Routledge, 1967).
[9] D. F. Thomson, "Fatherhood in the Wik Monkan Tribe," *American Anthropologist*, Vol. 38 (1936), pp. 374–93.

and since, as Thomson says, the matter is of interest and importance, I propose a discussion of his paper with a view to indicating something of the difficulties with which the ethnological mind has to contend when confronted with a matter ostensibly so simple as the determination of whether or not a particular people make a connection between intercourse and childbirth.

In an extremely interesting paper on the Koko Ya'o and neighboring tribes on the east coast of Cape York Peninsula,[10] Thomson stated that these tribes possessed a knowledge of physiological paternity, the child being regarded as the product of the seminal fluid of the father, whereas the mother was regarded as "nothing."

Thomson appears to have been under the impression that such findings were unique for any Australian tribe, but as long ago as 1893 B. H. Purcell reporting on the Workii, a tribe who live not far distant to the northwest of the Cape York peoples, made known the existence of a very similar belief in the virtues of seminal fluid. Thus he writes in connection with the Bora ceremony:

> After the third initiation into this remarkable ceremony the youth is made to drink semen that is taken from six or as many young clean gins and blacks as may be in the camp at the Bora ground. No gins are admitted to the ceremony other than these. When an old man is dying, they do exactly the same. They hold that as semen brought them into the world, it should keep them alive and from dying; and when a man dies they think that the semen germinates and even comes through the earth again and appears in the form of a white man or something else, often a star.[11]

Writing in 1931, Professor W. Lloyd Warner gives an account of his experiences among the tribes of northern Arnhem Land,

10 D. F. Thomson, "The Hero Cult, Initiation and Totemism on Cape York," *Journal,* Royal Anthropological Institute, Vol. 63 (1933), pp. 453–537.

11 B. H. Purcell, "Rites and Customs of Australian Aborigines," *Verhandlungen, Berliner Gesellschaft für Anthropologie,* Vol. 25 (1893), pp. 286–89.

North Australia. During his first nine months of work among them he "could find no indication of any knowledge whatsoever about physiological conception," yet "there were strong indications that there was an understanding of the true nature of the physical function of the father."

> The second time [writes Professor Warner] I entered the area I determined to go into this matter further, since the people I studied were but a continuation of the central tribes on which Spencer and Gillen reported. An occasion arose in which I could inquire directly of certain old men just what the semen did when it entered the uterus of a woman. They all looked at me with much contempt for being so ignorant and informed me that "that was what made babies." [12]

Thus when Thomson published his first paper, there were already in existence at least two separate and independent accounts for the general region reported upon by Thomson of tribes possessing a knowledge of the role played by the seminal fluid in producing conception.

Thomson has taken great pains to show, and he has done so very successfully, the considerable effects produced by Papuan cultural influences upon Cape York culture. But what neither he nor Professor Warner has taken any pains to point out is that for many years this region has also been steadily infiltrated by appreciable white influences. Apart from the possibility that the tribes in this general region may have acquired their "knowledge" of the virtues of seminal fluid from Papuan sources, for which the evidence is exceedingly strong, we have also to reckon with the possibility that these tribes may have acquired this knowledge, in part at least, from white sources. In this connection, W. E. H. Stanner, reporting on the Daly River tribes of North Australia, has some illuminating remarks. He writes:

[12] W. Lloyd Warner, "Birth Control in Primitive Society," *Birth Control Review*, Vol. 4 (1931), pp. 105–7.

It is clear ... that two theories of sex exist side by side: (a) a mystical theory of the type commonly found in Australian cultures, and (b) a barely understood, confused version of orthodox theory learned from whites. The emphasis in belief ranges from tribes like the Mulluk Mulluk and Madngella, which have completely forgotten their own mystical theory (which undoubtedly existed) to bush tribes with only the most imperfect knowledge of white beliefs. In tribes (like the Marithiel) where the beliefs co-exist in some definite form, the framing of the question governs the answer one receives. ... In the pure native theory the sexual act seems to have mostly an erotic significance, but in the altered belief it is considered to be in some way concerned with pregnancy. How or why is not known.[13]

Lauriston Sharp, reporting on the Yir-Yiront, who live along the western coast of Cape York Peninsula in the vicinity of the mouth of the Coleman River, states that according to native belief "children are sent out from spirit centres only when people copulate; but it is not the intercourse, but rather the immigration of the 'spirit child' which causes a pregnancy." [14]

Ursula McConnel, reporting on the Koko-yalunyu of the Bloomfield River district, North Queensland, writes: "The Koko-yalunyu quite definitely consider sex-contact to be necessary to child-bearing. They frankly admit, however, that they do not understand *in what way* it is necessary." [15] An eponymous ancestress "sends all the babies to their mothers and so is the mystic cause in individual cases." [16]

It is apparent that among these peoples intercourse is recognized as having some connection with pregnancy, but precisely what connection remains obscure to them, and would not, it seems, be of much concern to the native. Intercourse is vaguely

---

13 W. E. H. Stanner, "The Daly River Tribes, a Report of Field Work in North Australia," *Oceania,* Vol. 4 (1933), pp. 10–29.

14 L. Sharp, "Ritual Life and Economics of the Yir-Yiront of Cape York Peninsula," *Oceania,* Vol. 5 (1934), pp. 19–42.

15 U. McConnel, "A Moon Legend from the Bloomfield River, North Queensland," *Oceania,* Vol. 2 (1931), pp. 9–25.

16 *Ibid.*

regarded as a condition which makes the entry of a spirit child into a woman possible, but clearly the spirit child is not regarded as deriving from either the father or the mother to whom it is born, but is considered to originate from an ancestral source. Incidentally, it may be mentioned that in the region of which Miss McConnel writes, white settlers have been permanently established for nearly a century. Yet writing in 1893 of the tribes in this region, W. E. Roth was able to find no evidence of a belief in any sort of a connection between intercourse and childbirth. It is, of course, nonetheless possible that the belief existed and escaped Roth's attention, for there is good reason to believe that the belief in a connection between intercourse and childbirth is universally present among the tribes of Australia, apart altogether from any question of contamination by white influences.

It has generally been overlooked that Spencer and Gillen stated that such a connection was recognized among the Central tribes investigated by them; here are their own words:

> ... We have amongst the Arunta, Luritcha, and Ilpirra tribes, and probably also amongst others such as the Warramunga, the idea firmly held that the child is not the direct result of intercourse, that it may come without this, which merely, as it were, prepares the mother for the reception and birth also of an already formed spirit child who inhabits one of the local totem centres. Time after time we have questioned them on this point, and always received the reply that the child was not the direct result of intercourse.[17]

If these words mean anything, they mean that it is the general belief among Arunta and neighboring Central tribes that intercourse is necessary before a spirit child will enter a woman, although it is considered that in certain cases it is possible for a woman to be entered by a spirit child without the preliminary preparation of intercourse.

[17] Spencer and Gillen, *The Native Tribes of Central Australia*, p. 22.

Strehlow [18] and Fry [19] have independently confirmed Spencer and Gillen's findings in this connection among the Arunta and Loritja as well as among neighboring tribes.

It will be recalled that Malinowski found a recognition of a precisely similar connection between intercourse and the entry of a spirit child into the woman among the Trobriand Islanders, who were shown by Malinowski to have no knowledge of the relationship between intercourse and conception.[20] Among the Trobrianders, as among the Australians, intercourse is regarded merely as a preparer of the woman for the reception of a spirit child, but it is not in any way regarded as the cause of conception.

It may well be asked whether this recognition of intercourse as a preparer of the woman does not constitute the strongest evidence that the animistic beliefs have simply pushed the knowledge of the bare physiological facts out of the way. The world of the Australian is a spiritual world, and material acts are invested with a spiritual significance. Human beings have a long spiritual history behind them, and the spiritual source of every member of the tribe is known. The spiritual origin of children is the fundamental belief and among the most important stays of the social fabric. It would be absurd then to think, in the face of such knowledge, that an act such as intercourse could be the cause of a child. In a vague sort of way the Australian knows that without intercourse there will not, as a rule, be a child, but at the same time he knows that intercourse is the least important factor in the whole cycle of events. Intercourse is a condition, and a dispensable condition, but is never the cause of conception. Such facts, I suggest, render unnecessary any assumption that the animistic beliefs have been re-

18 C. Strehlow, *Die Aranda- und Loritja-Stämme in Zentral Australien* (Frankfurt, 1907–1921), Part 3, pp. x–xiii.

19 H. K. Fry, "Body and Soul, a Study from Western Central Australia," *Oceania*, Vol. 3 (1933), pp. 247–56.

20 Malinowski, *The Sexual Life of Savages.*

sponsible for the repression or elimination of a preexisting knowledge of the facts. What such beliefs do secure is a state of mind, of affective-imaginative associations, which assist to make the establishment of a significant relationship between intercourse and conception virtually impossible, and there is no good reason to believe that this state of affairs was ever otherwise, that intercourse was ever recognized to play a more significant role in the production of conception than it does today. In short, though a great deal of energy and ingenuity has been expended in arguing the point, and by no means unattractively, that such beliefs as the Central Australians are alleged to hold in connection with the process of procreation are not primitive but are the result of their spiritual philosophy which has caused the knowledge of the relationship between intercourse and childbirth to become gradually repressed, the connection cropping out of the tufa of consciousness in the demoted form of a purely ancillary act in the service of a spiritual function, I do not think that anyone has thus far succeeded in making out a case beyond what is purely speculative. As I have already indicated, I do not consider that there is a single factor of whatsoever nature in any Australian culture which upon examination would lead one to believe that the Australian aborigines ever knew more than they do today of the connection between intercourse and childbirth: the probability is that they knew much less.

Thomson writes:

> The Wik Monkan recognizes, and freely affirms, the fertilizing influence of seminal fluid (tänkärrä), but on the physiological aspect of conception and pregnancy, his knowledge is less exact. He recognizes that pregnancy results from the introduction of seminal fluid, but as to how the embryo is produced, his ideas are as vague as those of any white man who possesses no biological knowledge. His belief is that the seminal fluid enters the uterus (po'o mompa) and gradually builds up the body of the embryo, and thus he insists that a single sexual act is not sufficient to

produce conception, which can result only from repeated inter-course.[21]

Thomson's facts are not in question, but the role which the seminal fluid is believed to play in building up the body of the embryo reads suspiciously like the New Guinea notion of these things. Similarly the belief that it is necessary for the father to lie repeatedly with the mother that the body may be built up during the prenatal period is a widespread New Guinea belief, occurring also over a wide area of Melanesia.

Thomson describes the Wik Monkan notions of conception in some detail (p. 377), and these indicate that this tribe is quite well informed concerning the mechanism of conception and the changes which follow it.

It is to be noted, however, that the Wik Monkan notion of the relationship between intercourse and conception is really quite shaky, for they are unaware that a single act of coitus is sufficient to produce conception; they insist on the necessity of repeated acts before conception can be produced. It is, of course, quite possible that they have acquired this notion empirically, though it seems difficult to believe this. What would seem to be nearer the truth is that at one time the procreative beliefs of the peoples of this region were of the same general pattern as those encountered throughout the rest of Australia and that the present beliefs of the Wik Monkan and neighboring tribes have been acquired lock, stock, and barrel from their Papuan neighbors, with a possible recent addition from white sources. Whereas Thomson has fully emphasized the considerable influ-ence of Papuan hero cults "that had modified considerably the indigenous culture" (p. 374) of the eastern tribes of Cape York Peninsula, he has somehow failed to take into consideration the possibility that the Cape York procreative beliefs, which con-stitute so striking an aberration from the general Australian pattern, may be attributed to the same modifying influences of

21 Thomson, "Fatherhood in the Wik Monkan Tribe," p. 375.

the indigenous culture as have affected practically its every aspect.

It seems to me clear that if we admit, as I believe we must, that everywhere else in Australia the fertilizing influence of seminal fluid is not in any way understood, then it follows that wheresoever in Australia there does exist such a knowledge this is probably of extra-Australian origin.

Thus, while we may accept Thomson's statement that physiological paternity is recognized among the Wik Monkan and neighboring tribes of Cape York Peninsula, it must at the same time also be recognized that the conditions in this part of the continent are unique, and that they cannot in any way be generalized for the rest of Australia.

Thomson writes:

> On account of the controversial nature of the subject, and the fact that the knowledge of physiological paternity is in conflict with the findings of previous workers both to the north and south of this region, considerable care was exercised in the collection and checking of information and in the testing of informants (p. 391).

But there is here no conflict. Surely each tribe may be allowed to enjoy its own particular version of the nature of things without its being described by an intruding ethnologist as in conflict with the beliefs of some other tribe whom he has arbitrarily elected as the standard of reference? I do not see where any question of conflict arises here. Had a number of independent workers reporting on the same horde of the same tribe given conflicting versions of the conditions found by them the matter would be different, but such a case has not arisen, and it is therefore difficult to understand Thomson's remarks in this connection.

Thomson feels "that the ignorance of physical paternity was taken for granted by many of the early workers who had come under the influence of 'group marriage' beliefs" (p. 392).

But the truth is that the most highly trained and intelligent workers of more recent years, who have been completely divorced from anything like "group marriage" beliefs, have also found this nescience to prevail among the tribes investigated by them. In the exceptional cases in which there has been some doubt it could be demonstrated (I am not referring to the Cape York and neighboring tribes) that mission or other white influences had been at work.

The fancied incompatibility which Thomson sees between his own findings in North Australia and Malinowski's conviction—which he thinks, mistakenly, to be based upon the latter's Trobriand experiences—that ignorance of physiological paternity is an original feature of primitive psychology does not exist.

The Trobrianders, Thomson would appear to argue, are clearly a culturally more advanced people than the Cape York peoples, yet among the one it is stated that a knowledge of physiological paternity does not exist, whereas in the other this knowledge demonstrably exists. Hence it is somewhat strange that since the less advanced people possess the knowledge the more advanced people should not possess it. It would seem, therefore, runs Thomson's argument, that the nescience cannot be primitive. Thomson writes in his final paragraph:

> The existence of this knowledge of physical paternity, which has a fundamental character, in this region lying midway between the areas of Central Australia and Papua, where such beliefs are said to be absent, presents some difficulties. The conclusion that seems to be inevitable is that the ignorance of physical paternity is not primitive but that, as Professor Carveth Read suggested,[22] where it does exist at the present time among primitive peoples, true knowledge has been masked by animistic beliefs, superimposed upon the primitive condition. I consider that the evidence now presented from the Wik Monkan tribe is conclusive, and that if such knowledge is absent from more primitive

22 "No Paternity," *Journal, Royal Anthropological Institute,* Vol. 48 (1918), pp. 146–54.

people to the south, and from the more advanced peoples to the north, the facts admit of no other conclusion (p. 393).

Apart from the numerous objections which such an argument at once raises, the simple fact that there is every reason to believe that the Cape York peoples obtained their knowledge of the nature of procreation from an extraneous cultural source already in possession of it, is alone sufficient to explain how it may come about that a culturally less advanced people may be in the possession of knowledge not in the possession of an otherwise culturally more advanced group.

It is hardly correct to state that in Papua a knowledge of physiological paternity, or the connection between intercourse and conception, is "said to be absent." As far as I am aware no one has thus far reported such a state of affairs among any Papuan people: on the contrary, such reports as we have of them show that their knowledge of the nature of procreation is practically identical with such a knowledge as Thomson has reported for the Wik Monkan. Thomson's argument that since the Cape York peoples are, as it were, in a geographic position intermediate between the Central Australians and the Papuans, it is more than likely that the Cape York peoples present the truly fundamental primitive conditions of knowledge on the subject of procreation, and that among the peoples to the north and south of them there has been a masking of the original fundamental knowledge, therefore defeats itself.

I submit that the facts lead to a conclusion quite opposite to that arrived at by Thomson.

22. *Ignorance of Physiological Paternity in Secular Knowledge and Orthodox Belief Among the Australian Aborigines*

In my book on the Australian aborigines [1] I examined the evidence relating to the procreative beliefs of the Australian aborigines, both living and extinct, with a view to determining whether or not any or all of the native tribes of Australia were actually ignorant of the fact that sexual intercourse is the primary necessary link in the whole chain of events which lead to the production of pregnancy and childbirth in the female. It was found that on the basis of the available evidence there could be little doubt that some tribes, at least, were probably unaware of this fact, while in some other tribes the evidence was doubtful. It was shown that in no case was the evidence of such a nature as to permit the establishment of an indisputable conclusion concerning the actual nature of this ignorance, but assuming that in some tribes a complete ignorance of the true relationship between intercourse and childbirth did exist, our

[1] M. F. Ashley Montagu, *Coming into Being Among the Australian Aborigines* (London, 1937; New York, 1938).

task was to discover how such a nescience of the facts could possibly be maintained in such groups. We found upon investigation that on the positive side there was much in the experience of the aboriginal which would tend to make possible and to support such a nescient interpretation of the facts of procreation, and on the negative side there was absolutely nothing in his experience which would in any way be incompatible with such an interpretation. As far as the possibility of such a nescience was concerned, it was shown that all the conditions of possibility were more than adequately fulfilled; there was nothing in the least mysterious in these conditions, and one did not have to think of the intelligent native as an imbecile in order to conceive of the possibility of such a nescience. Within the framework of demonstrated possibility we had, then, merely to deal with the question of the possibility of the nescience of procreation's being a real nescience, as reported by the majority of investigators, or else a religiosocial phrasing of orthodox doctrine which serves to obscure the secular knowledge of the facts. We found in favor of the nescience's being a real and not a false one. It represented not so much a failure to recognize the facts as a specific social interpretation given to these facts both in secular and in orthodox life, which made such a nescience possible. It was not, however, a matter, as Andrew Lang put it, of psychology obscuring physiology, but as far as human beings were concerned, physiology did not enter into the question at all and social psychology was the determining, and the sole determining, point here.

Knowledge is never more than what it is socially determined to be, and if certain sense data are intellectually interpreted in a particular manner, that interpretation constitutes the knowledge of such sense data. I have pointed out *ad nauseam* that the aborigines are aware of the fact that intercourse is a necessary factor in the production of childbirth, but that they do not consider it to be of any great importance in the production of such a condition. Intercourse is not a cause of childbirth; it is merely a preparative act for the reception of a spirit baby. This clearly means that a relationship between intercourse and childbirth is recognized; but what is understood of that relationship is of such a nature that it would appear to be quite as definitely possible to say that the aboriginal has no knowledge of the value or importance of intercourse in the whole process inherent in that relationship. In that sense he is nescient or ignorant of the facts of procreation.

Under another type of social conditioning, the Australian aborigines would undoubtedly prove as capable as anyone else of recognizing the facts of procreation, but it so happens that they live within a social framework which renders such knowledge of no functional value whatever and, on the other hand, places an emphasis on a kind of knowledge which is both contrary and contradictory to the physiological facts. Under such conditions such knowledge as exists relating to the facts of procreation must be regarded as the efficient factual knowledge which each individual socially receives as the "truth" concerning the nature of the procreative process.

What I should like to emphasize here is that no one, even at this late date, knows exactly what those Australian tribes who are alleged to be ignorant of the facts of procreation do and do not know about such facts. We have a certain amount of evidence, but from a rigorously scientific point of view this is not as satisfactory as it might be. This evidence has been discussed in my book, and I have already stated here some of the conclusions which we were able to draw from it. Such conclusions must be regarded as subject to confirmation and must await the judgment of the fieldworker who has devoted his special attention to the solution of this problem. In spite of all statements to the contrary we do not know what the Australian aboriginal really believes about the procreative process.

What is greatly desirable is that native tribes who have been completely untouched by any white or Melanesian influences shall be made the subject of investigation calculated to reveal whether or not the members of such tribes possess a secular knowledge of the facts of procreation which does or does not form a part of their orthodox belief. If it can be shown in a particular uncontaminated tribe that the facts of procreation are secularly known, but are in orthodox belief rejected, then it becomes certain of such a tribe that their so-called nescience of the facts of procreation represents no more than an orthodox myth. This, in fact, is the interpretation which has been given to the evidence by many students of the subject, including Andrew Lang,[2] Goldenweiser,[3] Westermarck,[4] Read,[5] Warner,[6] Róheim,[7] Thomson,[8] Elkin,[9] Mountford,[10] and the Berndts.[11]

Róheim has gone so far as to suggest that the nescience is due to an active process of repression which takes its origin in one phase of the Oedipus complex, *i.e.*, in the unconscious hostility between father and son, in the hostility of the child toward the father who killed the animal from which it originated.[12] I have pointed out elsewhere [13] that the cause which Róheim gives

[2] A. Lang, *The Secret of the Totem* (London, 1905), p. 190.

[3] A. Goldenweiser, review of Hartland's *Primitive Paternity*, in *American Anthropologist*, N.S., Vol. XIII (1911), p. 598.

[4] E. Westermarck, *The History of Human Marriage*, Vol. I (London, 1922), p. 293.

[5] C. Read, "No Paternity," *Journal of the Royal Anthropological Institute*, Vol. XLVII (1918), p. 145.

[6] W. Lloyd Warner, "Birth Control in Primitive Society," *Birth Control Review*, Vol. XV (1931), p. 105; *A Black Civilization* (New York, 1937), p. 23.

[7] G. Róheim, "Psycho-Analysis of Primitive Cultural Types," *International Journal of Psycho-Analysis*, Vol. XIII (1932), p. 96; "Women and Their Life in Central Australia," *Journal of Royal Anthropological Institute*, Vol. LXIII (1933), p. 241.

[8] D. F. Thomson, "The Hero Cult, Initiation, and Totemism on Cape York," *Journal of the Royal Anthropological Institute*, Vol. LXIII (1933), p. 460; "Fatherhood in the Wik Monkan Tribe," *American Anthropologist*, N.S., Vol. XXXVIII, p. 374.

[9] A. P. Elkin, *The Australian Aborigines* (New York, 1964).

[10] C. P. Mountford, *Brown Men and Red Sand* (London, 1950).

[11] R. M. and C. H. Berndt, *The World of the First Australians* (Chicago, 1964).

[12] G. Róheim, "The Nescience of the Aranda," *British Journal of Medical Psychology*, Vol. XVII (1938), p. 343.

[13] M. F. Ashley Montagu, "Science, Nescience, and Psycho-Analysis," *British Journal of Medical Psychology*, Vol. XVIII (1941), p. 383.

for such a process of repression represents but one of the many ways in which children are believed to come into being, and that Róheim would seem merely to have selected the evidence to fit his theory. Actually Róheim writes, "The identity in their minds of the child with a being who was killed by the father before the child was born is an *expression* of the unconscious hostility between father and son, i.e., of one aspect of the Oedipus complex" (italics mine). Here the unconscious hostility clearly is made to produce the identification of the child with the being who was killed by the father; it is a rendering possible, by repression, of the relations between father and child. In the same manner we would suppost Róheim to interpret the belief that the child owes its being to the fact that as a spirit baby it entered its mother from a tree or some other object situated in the father's territory. Obviously, when the child realizes that it owes its existence to its father there can be no hostility between them. Such a belief is the gloss which the unconscious renders possible for the conscious mind.

Such an interpretation of the facts is by no means unacceptable, but it lacks confirmation by other independent investigators. Fieldworkers would do well to bear this theory in mind.

Contradictory beliefs, it is well known, may exist side by side in the mind of the individual and in the beliefs of a society without ever coming into conflict with one another. In our own society it is possible for one and the same individual, or for the group as a whole, to believe in the truth of both the theory of evolution and the book of Genesis, in the equality and the inequality of individuals, in miracles and the laws of physical causality, and so on; and such views may, and indeed usually are, successfully reconciled with one another. For societies more primitive than our own, Lévy-Bruhl has voluminously cited the evidences of similar processes of thought and has expended much labor and ingenuity in the attempt to show that the principle of contradiction in such societies is frequently not recognized.[14] As among ourselves, so among simpler peoples things that are unequal to one another are often equal to the same thing, and vice versa. Indeed, the permutations and combinations which human thought may take are limitless. The problem that it is immediately desirable to solve in connection with the Australian aborigines is whether or not contrary or contradictory beliefs are held in one and the same tribe concerning the nature of procreation, whether upon this point secular knowledge fundamentally differs from orthodox belief.

[14] L. Lévy-Bruhl, *How Natives Think* (London, 1926); *The "Soul" of the Primitive* (London, 1928); *Primitives and the Supernatural* (London, 1935); La Mythologie Primitive (Paris, 1935).

23. *Ignorance of Physiological Maternity in Australia*

There is a difference between the recognition of the fact that a child develops from an egg produced by the mother and the idea that a child develops from a "spirit child" which is produced by, and enters her from, an external source. A recognition of the first fact constitutes an awareness of the essential physiological nature of maternity, while a nonrecognition or rejection of this interpretation of the nature of maternity and an acceptance of the second notion obviously constitutes a non-physiological, spiritistic interpretation of maternity.

Many millions of eggs are every day hatched in incubators, but no one believes that the incubator is genetically or physiologically related to the chick in the sense in which the hen is which gave it birth. While studying the literature descriptive of the procreative beliefs of the Australian aborigines, the evidence gradually forced on my attention the probability that the aborigines conceptualized the actual generative process in much the same terms as those in which we think of the relationship between incubator and chick. The incubator enables the egg in which the already predetermined undeveloped chick lies to develop into a chick, but it has no more connection with the generation of the egg than it has with the predetermined character of the chick.

As I have already said, a consideration of the Australian material suggested to me that it was much in this way that the aborigines looked upon the development and birth of a child. The mother was merely the incubator of a "spirit child" (*pace,* egg) which very definitely originated from a source *physiologically* quite unrelated to her own body. This is what I meant, and mean, by "ignorance of physiological maternity" in my book on the procreative beliefs of the Australian aborigines.[1]

When a group or an individual affirms belief that in the generation of a child the female, who subsequently gives it birth, plays no role other than that of housing it and supplying it with nutriment during the time of its "unfolding," such a belief can only be pronounced as unphysiological. In reality the word "unphysiological" is quite unsatisfactory here, since the notion that the predetermined externally originating spirit child is supplied with nourishment during its stay in the mother's womb is certainly a physiological conception, and insofar as this belief prevails in any group, the woman who gives birth to a child must be said to be physiologically related to it in the sense that she supplied it with nourishment during its sojourn in her womb. In this sense the incubator is physiologically related to the chick hatched from the egg which was placed within it for that purpose by some external agency. There is no *genetic* relationship among egg, chick, and incubator, or among spirit child, mother, and offspring, and it is in this genetic sense that a physiological relationship between mother and child can be said to pass unrecognized among the Australian aborigines. This is what I mean by ignorance of physiological maternity.

Since some writers [2] have taken me to task for asserting what I have never stated, and since "evidence" has been produced to prove the existence of facts and knowledge concerning the relationship between mother and child which I have myself

[1] M. F. Ashley Montagu, *Coming into Being Among the Australian Aborigines* (London, 1937).
[2] I am unable to deal with all of them here.

asserted to exist, it would seem that some further discussion of my views concerning the ignorance of physiological maternity is necessary.

Professor A. R. Radcliffe-Brown,[3] Dr. Geza Róheim,[4] Dr. Phyllis Kaberry,[5] and Dr. Ralph Piddington [6] have recently criticized my views on the grounds that to say that an Australian child does not know its own mother is ridiculous. "We need not take the trouble even to refute such a view." [7] I thoroughly agree—all the more so since I have never stated that an Australian child does not know its own mother. Every child unquestionably knows its own mother. In my book I wrote—and Radcliffe-Brown quotes the passage—"Certainly it is quite clear to every Australian that each child passes into this world through the medium of some woman, and there is no one who would or could deny that this elementary fact is quite clearly recognized by the native. What the native does deny . . . is that there exists any tie of blood between a child and the woman out of whom it has come." [8]

Upon this passage Radcliffe-Brown comments as follows: "Since this is precisely what my statement means, I am completely at a loss to understand why the author should censure me for saying what he says himself." [9] He goes on to say, "One has to try to guess what 'tie of blood' may mean, and more particularly what it might mean to an Australian black fellow, since this is what he is declared to deny." [10] In the first sentence

---

[3] A. R. Radcliffe-Brown, *Man*, Vol. XXXVIII, Nos. 12–14 (Jan., 1938), pp. 15–16 (to which the proper reply is, in the words of Buffon in a similar situation, "*Il faut laisser la calomnie retomber sur elle-même*").

[4] Geza Róheim, "The Nescience of the Aranda," *British Journal of Medical Psychology*, Vol. XVII (1938), pp. 343–60.

[5] Phyllis Kaberry, *Aboriginal Woman* (London, 1939).

[6] Ralph Piddington, *Man*, Vol. XL, No. 112 (June, 1940), p. 92.

[7] Geza Róheim, Review of *Coming into Being Among the Australian Aborigines* in *British Journal of Medical Psychology*, Vol. XVII (1938), pp. 379–80.

[8] Montagu, *op. cit.*, p. 309.

[9] Radcliffe-Brown, *loc. cit.*

[10] *Ibid.*

the reference is to my criticism of Radcliffe-Brown's statement: "There is an obvious physiological relationship between a woman and the child to which she gives birth." [11] I maintained, as I still do, that it is difficult to see upon what grounds such a knowledge of physiological maternity could be attributed to the Australians, since as Radcliffe-Brown had himself shown in the same essay, "The Australian aborigines do not recognize physiological but only social relationships." [12] In a footnote to this sentence I suggested that "this statement would indicate that our disagreement here resolves itself purely to a matter of definition." [13] And that is clearly to what the misunderstanding is due. Before proceeding to discuss this matter, it is necessary to point out here that Radcliffe-Brown's statement: "One has to guess what 'tie of blood' may mean," is hardly justified in view of my statement, and the discussion which follows it, on page 310 of my book: "To recognize, or to become aware of the existence of such a thing as *blood-relationship,* one individual at least must be regarded as in a particular sense the cause of another, it must be recognized that some part of the one has contributed to the formation, to the genesis, of the other." Only between individuals recognizing such relationships could a "tie of blood" be said to exist. Surely, this is a clear enough definition of what I mean by "tie of blood"? In the succeeding sentence I stated that the Australians had no conception of such operative *causes,* and hence that the concept of consanguinity was impossible to them. This is the notion of "tie of blood" which the blackfellow was held not so much to deny as to ignore, and of which he has no awareness. For some inexplicable reason, Radcliffe-Brown appears to have omitted any reference to pages 310–11, in which these matters are fully dealt with, though he

[11] A. R. Radcliffe-Brown, "The Social Organization of Australian Tribes," *Oceania,* Vol. I (1930), p. 42.
[12] *Ibid.,* p. 43.
[13] Montagu, *op. cit.,* p. 313, note 2.

quotes four pages, 309–12, where the passages to which he takes exception occur.[14]

Where the misunderstanding has arisen is quite evident from Radcliffe-Brown's statement: "I should have thought that it was evident that the physiological relation to which I referred as being obvious is the fact that a child comes into the world out of the body of the mother and is not found under a gooseberry bush." [15]

Of course, everyone knows that "a child comes into the world out of the body of the mother," but no one for a moment believes that the child was *produced* or *created* in the body of the woman from which it has issued. The belief is rather that an already *preformed* spirit child has entered her from some external source, generally, but neither always nor necessarily associated in some way with her husband. A child is not physiologically produced in a woman, and physiologically the male has nothing to do with its production—the latter is merely the means of causing a *particular* spirit child to migrate *into* a woman. Children are not *physiologically produced* by anyone; they are conceived to have been created at a far distant time, and human beings play absolutely no physiological part in their generation. Such a view of the process of coming into being is certainly both nongenetic and unphysiological.

In my book I showed that intercourse was everywhere in Australia considered a necessary factor in bringing about the immigration of a spirit child into a woman, but that intercourse was nowhere considered a cause of pregnancy. Similarly, a woman is a necessary part of the process of pregnancy and childbirth, a necessary condition in the same sense as intercourse and a particular man—usually the husband—are necessary conditions. Neither the role of the male nor the role of intercourse

14 It is possible that they suffered the fate which Radcliffe-Brown, in a "review" of my book in *Nature*, Vol. CXLI (1938), pp. 263–64, visited upon a line of type which he incorrectly states to have been dropped from the place in which it is to be found!

15 Radcliffe-Brown, *Man*, *loc. cit.*

constitutes the crucial factor in any judgment concerning their awareness of physiological paternity and physiological maternity.

Neither intercourse nor childbirth is considered as the *cause* of a child's appearance in the group. Both intercourse and childbirth are necessary factors before it can be born. In this sense a child is no more *physiologically* related to a certain man than it is to a certain woman, merely because the one had intercourse with the woman and the other gave birth to the child. Certainly while the child always looks upon the woman out of whose body he came as his own mother, the man with whom she had intercourse prior to conception is not necessarily regarded as his own father. This is in itself only a recognition of the fact that he is so related to his "mother." But this does not imply any necessary recognition of a *physiological* relationship between them. The child is nourished while in the womb by whatever the mother eats, and particular items of diet may injure it during its sojourn there, but for all that the child is not regarded as having in any way been generated by the mother. She stands in the same physiological relationship to her child as the chick does to the incubator which hatched it. The real mother and father of the child are in the one case the eponymous ancestor who created all the spirit children in the long-distant "dream time," and in the other, the barnyard hen. Without the hen there would be no eggs. Without the ancestors there would be no spirit children. Without an incubator there would be no chicks. Without a mother there would be no means by which a spirit child could be born. The hen is the ancestor of the egg, but an Australian mother is not the ancestor of the egg which enters her from a totem center, and which she only serves to incubate.

As one of Howitt's natives put it, the mother is nothing; she is only a kind of wet nurse.[16] If this is what the Australian abo-

16 A. W. Howitt, *The Native Tribes of South-East Australia* (London, 1904), p. 195.

rigines believe, and all the evidence indicates that they do, then they are ignorant of physiological maternity.

Shortly after this paper was published, support for the views expressed in it came from the fieldwork of C. P. Mountford and A. Harvey on the Adnjamatana of northern South Australia, conducted during the years 1938–39.

These investigators write: "The Adnjamatana ... appear to have had no knowledge of physical paternity before the coming of the white man, and certain features of Adnjamatana theory ... suggest also the non-recognition of physiological maternity."

The evidence which Mountford and Harvey cite in support of this suggestion is as follows:

> First, the spirit-child which enters the woman is already an existent, complete and self-directing being that originated from a super-earthly source. It is able to find its own food and shelter. It also has the ability to choose for itself an earthly mother, and exercises freedom of choice among the women, subject only to the moiety rules. Stress is laid on the spirits' liking for fat and comely women. The second belief is that the *muri* (the spirit child) is independent of the mother during the period of gestation, this being indicated by the statement that after birth, it still has sufficient supplies of *amuruka* (spirit-child food-fruit of the *Jasminum lineare*) to sustain it for a period of equivalent to eight hours before suckling takes place.[17]

[17] C. P. Mountford and A. Harvey, "Women of the Adnjamatana Tribe of the Northern Flinders Ranges, South Australia," *Oceania,* Vol. 12 (1941), pp. 159–60.

24. *The Origin of Subincision*
in Australia

Subincision is a rite which, as is well known, is in Australia generally associated with the later stages of initiation. The rite was practiced over about three-quarters of the Australian continent (being absent from the eastern region and small areas in the far southwest of western Australia and the north of Arnhem Land). Basedow,[1] who has given us the most comprehensive study of subincision in Australia, and also Davidson,[2] have studied the distribution of this trait in some detail, but whereas Basedow concludes that the rite probably originated on the north coast of Australia,[3] Davidson is led to conclude that it probably originated in the central area.[4] As Davidson has pointed out,[5] the intense institutionalization of the rite in the central region, its complexity and uniform character, as compared with the superficial, simple, and very variable character of the rite as practiced among the peripheral peoples, would suggest a central origin for the rite. Basedow's conclusion that

[1] H. Basedow, "Subincision and Kindred Rites of the Australian Aboriginal," *Journal of the Royal Anthropological Institute*, Vol. LVII (1927), pp. 123–56.
[2] D. S. Davidson, *Chronological Aspects of Certain Australian Social Institutions* (Philadelphia, 1928), pp. 30–58.
[3] Basedow, *op. cit.*, p. 144.
[4] Davidson, *op. cit.*, p. 58.
[5] *Ibid.*

the rite probably originated on the north coast of Australia is not by any standard of logic or measurement a conclusion at all, but a premise based on the notion that subincision was devised in a region in which the male organ was most likely to become affected by inflammatory and microbic disorders; such a region would be the tropical north.[6] At best Basedow's hypothesis remains an unconvincing suggestion.

In central Australia, as well as in many other parts of the continent, the female is subjected to an operation similar to that of subincision at initiation. In the male the operation consists essentially in the slitting open of the whole or of a portion of the penile urethra along the ventral or undersurface of the penis. The initial cut is generally about an inch long, but this may be subsequently so enlarged as to extend from the glans to the root of the scrotum. In this way the whole of the underpart of the urethra is laid open. Here and there, especially in the southeast of the region, the intensity of the operation becomes reduced until one meets with forms which strongly resemble the condition of hypospadias, forms in which only a small slit is observable in the urethra situated either in the vicinity of the glans or of the scrotum, or at both places. In the female the operation takes a variety of forms, ranging from extensive laceration of the vaginal walls and clitoridectomy to the slightest laceration of as much of the hymen as may be present.

The operation of subincision has by many writers been regarded as a practice devised in order to limit the number of births. In other words, the practice is by these writers regarded as a contraceptive measure. If this were so, it would very strongly suggest that the relationship between intercourse and pregnancy was, at least at the time when the operation was originally introduced, fully understood. However, it remains more than doubtful whether the Australian aborigine has no such

6 Basedow, *op. cit.,* p. 144.

understanding of the physical relationship between intercourse and pregnancy.[7] Those who hold to the contraceptive theory are of the opinion that since the spermatic fluid normally passes through the urethra to the external orifice to be received by the vagina, the object of slitting the urethra is to cause the loss, through the incised portion of the urethra, of the spermatic fluid before it is able to reach the external orifice, so that during intercourse it would thus fail to reach the vagina.

To anyone acquainted with the anatomy and physiology of the male genital system, this theory, and the alleged facts upon which it is based, are so patently absurd as hardly to call for serious consideration. But since in the culture in which we live it is the custom to be least informed upon that subject concerning which every individual should know most, namely the structure and functions of his own body, it will perforce be necessary here to enter upon a discussion of the perhaps not altogether patent absurdities of this theory.

In the first place, it is to be noted that the force with which the spermatic fluid is launched into the penile urethra is very great.[8] This force has never been measured, but it is, at any rate, known that the ejaculated fluid is capable of traveling in space for a distance of as much as four feet or more after it has left the urethra, so that even with a considerably lacerated urethra it would not be unreasonable to suppose that some of this fluid, if not the greater part of it, would be projected through the external orifice. Certainly in connection with that form of subincision which is most commonly practiced in some parts of western Australia, in which a small incision is made in the urethra immediately anterior to the root of the scrotum, it is exceedingly unlikely that any but a small quantity of the

[7] I have devoted a full discussion to this matter in my book *Coming into Being Among the Australian Aborigines*.

[8] As Rabbi Schlomo Izchaki (Rashi) said in commenting on Genesis 49:26, "The seminal fluid spurts out like an arrow from its bow." See C. J. Brim, *Medicine in the Bible* (New York, 1936), p. 316.

spermatic fluid would find its way out through such an aperture, for the orifices of the ejaculatory ducts leading into the urethra are situated in the prostatic portion of the urethra, but a short distance posterior to the position that such an artificially made aperture would occupy. It is certain, therefore, that the force with which the spermatic fluid is normally projected through the ejaculatory ducts into the urethra would carry the greater part of it, at least, past this aperture without causing more than a little of it, if any, to be expressed through the latter. Those students who have concerned themselves with this subject and who are under the impression that during coitus the spermatic fluid is ejected through this aperture *extra vaginam* [9] must therefore be acquitted of any but the most innocent knowledge of the facts.

In the second place, even if the greater part of the spermatic fluid were to be expelled through the incised urethra during coitus, certainly most, if not all, of it would find its way into the vaginal canal. It should be recalled that the vagina of the female has generally also been lacerated, so that it forms quite a commodious chamber, which, together with the rhythmical muscular contraction of its walls, is capable of catching and holding all the spermatic fluid that is likely to escape in its proximity. The peculiar position adopted by the Australians during intercourse is calculated to ensure this. The position is thus described by Basedow:

> When a couple is about to indulge, the female, by request or habit, always takes her position by lying with her back upon the ground. The man squats between her legs, facing her, and lifts her thighs on to his hips. Leaning forwards, he steadies his body with his knees on the ground and accommodates the parts with his hands. This accomplished, the woman grips him tightly around his flanks or buttocks with her legs, while he pulls her towards his body with his hands around her neck or shoulders. [10]

9 *Vide*, for example, H. Aptekar, *Anjea* (New York, 1931), p. 124.
10 Basedow, *op. cit.*, p. 153.

As far as our present knowledge goes, the evidence indicates that this method of coition is practiced throughout Australia, in central, northern, and northwestern Australia, and in Queensland.[11] It should be obvious that this method of copulation is of such a nature that hardly any of the ejaculated spermatic fluid could possibly escape reaching the parts for which it was intended. Roth, for example, in this connection writes:

> The peculiar method of copulation in vogue throughout all these tribes does not prevent fertilization, notwithstanding the mutilation of the male. The female lies on her back on the ground, while the male with open thighs sits on his heels close in front: he now pulls her toward him, and raising her buttocks drags them into the inner aspects of his own thighs, her legs clutching him round the flanks, while he arranges with his hand the toilette of her perineum and the insertion of his penis. In this position the vaginal orifice, already enlarged by the general laceration at initiation, is actually immediately beneath and in close contact with the basal portion of the penis, and it is certainly therefore a matter of impossibility to conceive the semen as being discharged for the most part anywhere but into its proper quarter.[12]

Basedow writes:

> It is obvious that through the position adopted by the man a fair proportion of the ejected spermatic fluid will find its way into the vagina. In a state of erection, the mutilated organ becomes very wide; it is only natural that after the lower connecting wall of the urethral canal has been severed, the *corpus penis* in this condition spreads itself laterally ...
>
> Through this lateral distension, the receiving vagina will gape more than it would under normal conditions, and so there is

[11] W. E. Roth, *Ethnological Studies Among the North-West-Central Queensland Aborigines* (Brisbane and London, 1897), p. 179.
[12] *Ibid.*

greater facility for the fluid to enter. And more, the tribes who practise subincision in most cases also submit the female to a corresponding mutilation, which further dilates the passage.[13]

Since, then, it must be very apparent to the Australian that the spermatic fluid enters the vagina of the female, it is hardly credible that were he aware of the nature of that fluid and were he anxious to avoid the consequences of its action, he would have continued the use, had it ever been devised for the purpose, of a method at once so extremely painful and so utterly ineffectual in attaining the object attributed to it by those in whose imagination alone it seems ever to have had such an object. In this connection we may quote from Roth and Basedow once more.

"There is no tradition whatever," writes Roth, "and I have made searching inquiry, to the effect that introcision [14] is any preventive to procreation. When asked for an explanation, or the origin of the ordeal, the Aboriginals invariably plead ignorance or if pressed will answer somewhat to the effect that 'Mulkari [15] make him first time.' In this connection it is interesting to note that even the possibility of taking artificial means to prevent fertilization, etc. (I am not speaking of abortion), is apparently beyond their comprehension: thus I have reports from station managers who assure me that only with great difficulty could their 'boys' be made to understand, if they ever did, the object of spaying cattle." [16]

Roth further writes: "So far as my own observations go, I can positively state that the singular form of penile urethrotomy we are discussing (subincision) is not intended, nor anywhere

[13] Basedow, *op. cit.*, p. 155.
[14] This is another of the bewildering variety of names by which subincision is known; some others which have been commonly used are: division, *urethrotomia externa,* Sturt's rite, terrible or gruesome rite, artificial hypospadias, whistle, *mika, kulpi, arrilta, yerrupe,* etc.
[15] The supernatural guardian who makes everything the Boulia district natives cannot otherwise account for.
[16] Roth, *op. cit.*, p. 179.

regarded, by the Australian natives as a method of birth-control." [17]

The reason that has been suggested for the practice of sub-incision is that it is a method which was devised to ensure the maintenance of a proper balance between the food supply and the numbers of the population. This represents a purely fanci-ful speculation. Unfortunately for this theory, there are vast areas in Australia which are well capable of supporting a much larger proportion of individuals under normal conditions than are ever found in such territories. Furthermore, it is well to note that the rite of subincision is not limited to the hunger-stricken desert region tribes but is found away to the north and to the south among the tribes where food is plentiful and the population not, oftentimes, as large as among the desert tribes. Moreover, as Roth pointed out many years ago in respect of the tribes of northwest central Queensland,[18] the alleged object of this practice is already met by the universally strict observance of the laws regulating the sexual union of individu-als belonging to one or other moiety, class, and totem, whereby the quantity of food available to parents is in no way immedi-ately affected by the number of offspring. In all Australian tribes the consumption of every article of food is strictly regu-lated. Thus, speaking generally, the totem plant or animal of an individual is only on very rare occasions eaten by him, and then only very sparingly. A man will eat articles of food which are forbidden to his wife, and old men will eat many articles of food which are entirely forbidden to the younger people. In this way a most efficient equilibrium between the food supply and the number of individuals in the group is maintained, although it could hardly be called an equitable distribution from our point of view; but that is not the point.

Thus, it would seem clear that we must look elsewhere for an explanation of the meaning of subincision; that it has no con-

17 Basedow, *op. cit.*, p. 150.
18 Roth, *op. cit.*, p. 179.

nection with procreation or its control is abundantly clear, and with this demonstration the *pis aller,* one of the strongest of the evidences which have been cited in disproof of the Australian nescience of the relationship between intercourse and childbirth, vanishes. In what follows it is proposed to discuss subincision in terms of certain concrete evidence which would seem to give this curious practice a meaning it may very probably have originally possessed. In such matters, of course, there can be no question of proof or even of adequate demonstration; all that can at most be hoped for or expected is that the evidence be so pertinent and the conclusions to be deduced from it so cogent and reasonable as to afford the explanation thus obtained a degree of probability greater than that which any other explanation has heretofore succeeded in achieving.

It may at once be said that no theory which has thus far been advanced to account for the meaning of subincision has proven entirely acceptable. This has by no means been the fault of those students who have devoted their attention to the subject, for although a certain number of clues were available to them, there was nothing in their nature which could have enabled anyone to single them out from the mass of bewilderingly complicated details associated with the practice, in preference to certain other possible details which invited attention because of their similarity to those found in association with non-Australian peoples among whom various forms of subincision are also practiced. Among these peoples, chiefly the Fijians, the Tonga Islanders, and the natives of the Amazon basin of Brazil, subincision is carried out primarily as a therapeutic measure, and it is this possible therapeutic function of subincision that was seized upon as a clue to the significance of the practice among the Australians. Had the clue, which did not really become available until March, 1935, been accessible to those students who had concerned themselves with this subject, there can be little doubt that the explanation which is shortly to be offered for the significance of subincision would have been proposed ere now.

Among the Fijians it is believed that subincision is a preventive of many diseases and unless the individual submits himself to this operation he is likely to fall a victim to any of them at some time or another. The operation is also performed as a remedy following the onset of any of these disorders. It is also said to remove the evil humors of the body. Performed as a cure for tetanus among the Tongans, it is also resorted to in a variant form by passing a reed tube into the urethra in cases of general debility, and in the operative form with the object of removing the blood from the abdominal cavity produced by wounds in the abdomen.[19] From these practices and the motives for them, Rivers, who has devoted an extraordinarily interesting discussion to this subject, has concluded: "The operation acts as a counter-irritant and as a means of evacuating blood and possibly other bad humours, which are believed to be producing or helping to produce disease." [20] Hence, the motive for the practice is obviously therapeutic, a conclusion with which there can be no disagreement.

Among the Amazon River basin natives of Brazil, subincision is upon certain occasions practiced for the purpose of removing the diminutive fish which sometimes gain entry into the urethra while the natives are bathing in the waters in which these fish abound.[21] Here, too, it is therefore evident that the operation is of a purely therapeutic nature.

Such facts have led Basedow to suggest that the rite may have originated in Australia for similar reasons, since all sorts of crawling and burrowing crustaceans, insects, and other vermin, not to mention such things as splinters, burrs, grass seed, grit, and so forth, might easily gain entry into the urethra. Moreover, Basedow suggests that in tropical Australia, particularly in the north, where he thinks the practice may have originated, "acute inflammation of the prepuce, glans, and urethra might

19 W. Mariner, *Account of the Natives of the Tonga Islands* (London, 1817), Vol. II; Corney and Thomson, *The Fijians* (London, 1908).
20 W. H. R. Rivers, *Psychology and Ethnology* (London, 1926), p. 67.
21 K. von Steinen, *Durch Central Brazilien* (Leipzig, 1886).

periodically have seriously affected many of the male members of the tribe." [22]

Such a view of the origin of subincision in Australia may, of course, not be impossible, although it is somewhat strange that the operation is never practiced for such reasons among the natives of the present day but is instead regarded by them as a purely ceremonial rite. Rivers, however, has seen in the one factor associated with subincision common to the Fijians, the Tongans, and the Australians, namely the effusion of blood, a possible common origin for the practice. He offers two possible explanations for the appearance of subincision in islands so far removed from one another as Australia and Fiji. One is that the procedure of subincision belongs to the culture of a people who once occupied the whole of this part of Australia, and that the practice has only persisted in Fiji and certain parts of Australia, undergoing divergent lines of evolution which, in one or both places, have greatly modified its original purpose. Thus, it has become a purely therapeutic measure in one place and a purely magicoreligious rite in the other. In favor of this view Rivers, as indicating a possible physical relationship between the peoples concerned, states that very similar skulls occur in Viti Levu and Australia, skulls which bear a close resemblance to the ancient Neanderthal crania of Europe! We need not take this supporting statement very seriously, since the resemblances between the groups of crania named are at most of the most superficial kind.

The alternative hypothesis is that some migrant people, who practised subincision, either as a therapeutical practice or a ceremonial rite, introduced it into Fiji and Australia, and that in the process of assimilation into the indigenous culture of the two places it has undergone such transformation as now gives it its wholly different purpose in the two places. The special form of this hypothesis which seems the most likely to be true is that

22 Basedow, *op. cit.*, pp. 144–45.

a migrant people introduced the use of a urethra seton as a remedy for disease, and that this has largely maintained its original purpose in Fiji, while in Australia it has taken on the special magico-religious purpose, characteristic of the Aboriginal Australian culture. Having wholly lost all trace of its therapeutic purposes, it has become a purely ceremonial rite. There still, however, remains the effusion of blood, common to the two practices, which in the one place is the immediate motive, or one of the motives, of the therapeutic measure, while, in the other, it brings this rite into line with many other Australian rites in in which the effusion of blood plays so important a part.[23]

Neither of the hypotheses proposed by Rivers is inherently improbable, and indeed his first hypothesis derives some support from the fact that subincision has been described for two separate tribes in the Territory of New Guinea,[24] and the inhabitants of Wogeo, the most northerly of the Schouten Islands.[25] The most promising clue to the original meaning of the practice of subincision is afforded by the reasons which the investigator's informants gave for the practice among the latter people.

Against Rivers' hypotheses many objections have been urged, chief among which is the absence of subincision among the marginal tribes of Australia and the great intensification of the practice as one proceeds toward the center of the continent. The only marginal area in which subincision is found is in the south, and no one has so far been venturesome enough to suggest that any foreign influences may have come through that part of Australia. Davidson, who has very strongly argued against Rivers' theory on such grounds, thinks that the evidence of distribution is entirely against Rivers' first hypothesis.[26] But

[23] Rivers, *op. cit.,* pp. 68–69.

[24] R. Thurnwald, *Die Gemeinde der Banaro* (Stuttgart, 1921); cf. also *Zeit. f. Vergleich Rechtswissenschaft,* Bd. XXXVIII–XXXIX, pp. 21–22.

[25] H. I. Hogbin, "Native Culture of Wogeo: Report of Field Work in New Guinea," *Oceania,* Vol. V (1935), pp. 320–21.

[26] Davidson, *op. cit.,* pp. 45–58.

Professor A. P. Elkin, who has done much fieldwork in the northwestern as well as the central and southern parts of the continent, informs me that there is no difference in the intensity of the rite in these regions, and that in his opinion this practice, like a number of other customs, was diffused from the Kimberley region in a fanlike manner east and southeast. Incidentally, Professor Elkin says that circumcision is more "intense" in the northwest than in the center; in the former region the skin is removed from the whole of the penis. He adds that in all the subincision area subincision prepares the penis to be a source of ceremonial blood; this is obtained by causing a partial erection and then stabbing the subincised part.

Davidson finds that he cannot agree that the form of urethrotomy practiced among the Banaro is akin to the form practiced among the Australians, but to us it does not seem that the differences in the manner in which the operation is performed—among the Banaro two or three stems of a barbed grass are inserted into the urethra and then suddenly withdrawn, thus cutting open the walls of the urethra—are really important enough to rule the effects of the operation completely out of consideration as at all comparable. Had Davidson been willing to grant their comparability, he might not, perhaps, have argued as strongly as he has against the possible introduction of subincision into Australia by way of Melanesia in general and New Guinea in particular. The fact that subincision is unknown in the extreme north, including Melville and Bathurst Islands, does not constitute an objection to such a hypothesis, for it is quite possible that the peoples of these territories may once have practiced the rite, which may have been adopted from some migrant people, and subsequently discarded it. It should not be forgotten that these marginal peoples have probably been subject to more than one influx of foreigners, and like the reaction of the rocks to disturbing influences, their responses to these migrating influences must have been either conformable or nonconformable; in this way what at one time they may have adopted, they may well at another time have given up in favor of some other practice. In any case, there is Professor Elkin's view that subincision spread into Arnhem Land from the Kimberleys and that this and other customs were either evolved there or introduced into the continent by way of that region.

The element common to all forms of subincision is the invariable effusion of blood. This, as we have seen, has already been noted by Rivers, but it seems never to have occurred to him that the peculiar means adopted to produce this effusion, that is, the characteristic urethral incision of the male copulatory organ, might in some way be connected with the analogous natural effusion of the female from a similar source. Briefly, the suggestion here is that male subincision or incision corresponds, or is intended to correspond, to female menstruation. Indeed, the hypothesis may at once be stated which is about to be offered as an explanation of the probable origin of subincision in Australia; it is that *subincision in the male was originally instituted in order to cause the male to resemble the female with respect to the occasional effusion of blood which is naturally a characteristic of the female, and possibly, also, with respect to producing some feminization in the appearance of the male organ.*

As it stands, the theory must appear somewhat fantastic; we therefore hasten to produce the evidence upon which it is based.

It is perhaps necessary to point out in this place that among many Australian peoples menstruation is not regarded as a periodic occurrence but it is somewhat confusedly regarded as being a quite natural phenomenon, though of irregular occurrence, or as due to a cold in the head or other illness or to the scratching of an insect. Such are the beliefs, for example, which have been reported for the Arunta.[27] Among the Kakadua people of the Northern Territory menstruation appears to be regarded as a normal occurrence which is said to proceed from something which breaks near the heart and accumulates in the form of blood in a special bag inside, and it is when this bag bursts that the blood flows.[28] The taboos which in Australia are placed upon menstruating women and menstrual blood indicate that menstruation has always been regarded as a phenomenon to which some degree of mystery attaches. Menstrual blood everywhere among the Australian aborigines is regarded as unclean and as constituting an element of danger. Menstruating women must everywhere be avoided until they have got this dangerous element out of their bodies and are once again clean. It is the menstrual blood which is a sign of the uncleanness of the woman, and it is not until this noxious matter has been completely voided that the woman is thoroughly clean again. Menstrual blood is a noxious humor of mysteriously strong potency; this much is clear. Is it not possible, therefore, that judging this to be the natural or normal or most efficient manner of getting rid of the bad "humors" within one's body,[29] some early aborigines, upon the principle of like producing like, essayed to produce an artificial menstruation within their own bodies, and seeing that the blood came from the vulva in the female, what more natural then than to make it likewise come from the organ in one's own body that most closely corresponds to that organ in the female?

Interestingly enough, the only etymologies which it has been possible to trace for the meaning of the various words which are used to describe the subincised penis in Australia are those sup-

27 G. Róheim, "Women and Their Life in Central Australia," *Journal of the Royal Anthropological Institute*, Vol. LIII (1933), pp. 230–34.

28 B. Spencer, *Native Tribes of the Northern Territory of Australia* (London, 1914), p. 320.

29 Bloodletting has among most peoples been practiced for the same reason, and is still so practiced to this day among some of the peasantry of Europe. At one time, particularly in the seventeenth and eighteenth centuries, the treatment of almost every disease began with a phlebotomy or cupping.

plied by Roth and by Basedow. For the northwest central tribes of whom he writes, Roth states that "it is interesting to note that in the Pitta-Pitta and cognate Boulia district dialects the term used to describe an introcised penis denotes etymologically one with a vulva or 'slit.' " [30] Roth considered that female laceration preceded male subincision and that "on the principle of a form of mimicry, the analogous sign was inflicted on the male to denote corresponding fitness" for the purpose of copulation. In this Roth came very near to the theory which is here being proposed, but he fell somewhat wide of the mark because of his altogether unjustified assumption of the priority of female laceration. That the subincised penis is referred to as a vulva may or may not be of significance for the present theory; the interesting fact is offered here merely for what it may be considered to be worth. Among the Urrabuna of central Australia the operation of subincision is known as *yerrupe*. "The organ of the female," remarks Helms, "is therefore sometimes called by that name, although the proper name for the vagina is *pintha*." [31] Any value which may be placed upon such striking etymological synonymities derives some further support from the following interesting corroborative evidence.

Hogbin in his report on the people of Wogeo makes the following illuminating remarks:

> Perhaps the most fundamental religious conception relates to the difference between the sexes. Each sex is perfectly all right in its own way, but contact is fraught with danger for both. The chief source of peril is sexual intercourse, when contact is at its maximum. The juices of the male then enter the female and vice versa. Women are automatically cleansed by the process of menstruation, but men, in order to guard against disease, have periodically to incise the penis and allow a quantity of blood to flow. *This operation is often referred to as men's menstruation.* [32]

[30] Roth, *op. cit.*, p. 180.
[31] R. Helms, "Report of the Elder Expedition (Anthropology)," *Transactions of the Royal Society of South Australia,* Vol. XVI (1896), Pt. iii, p. 278.
[32] My italics.

All contact with a man or woman who is "menstruating" has to be avoided, and they themselves have to take a number of precautions. Thus they may not touch their own skin with their fingernails, and for a couple of days they have to eat with a fork. The penalty for touching a menstruating woman is death by a wasting disease, against which there is no remedy whatsoever. The "menstruating" man has also to avoid sexual intercourse until his wounds are healed, at least two months being allowed for this. Should this prohibition be broken both parties are likely to die, though they may save themselves by confessing their guilt and carrying out a magical rite.

Men also incise the penis after they have performed certain tasks which for magical reasons are held to be very dangerous. These include the erection of a new man's house, burying a corpse, taking part in an expedition with intent to murder someone, and initiating a youth. All these tasks are held in some mysterious manner to contaminate those who take part, and the flow of blood is necessary for cleansing purposes.[33]

Among the natives of Wogeo, then, it would appear quite clear that the penis is incised on the analogy of female menstruation for the purpose of permitting the bad humors of the body, and such as are likely to be produced during the performance of certain tasks with which a great deal of power is associated, to be liberated and voided.[34] Thus, the operation is here of a therapeutic and prophylactic nature, but it is at the same time a strongly magicoreligious procedure. The elements, then, that were missing in Basedow's and Rivers' theories are here supplied, and it seems highly probable, therefore, that whether or not the practice of subincision originated in Australia, whatever the reasons assigned by the natives for the practice, the rite as it is today practiced in that continent was originally performed for reasons similar to those given by the natives of Wogeo for their own rites of incision.

33 Hogbin, *op. cit.*, pp. 330–31.
34 It is of some interest to note that the Galenic conception of menstruation as a "plethora" was very similar to the Wogeo notion of menstruation.

25. *Infibulation and Defibulation in the Old and New Worlds*

Throughout the greater part of North Africa, including the region of the Nile cataracts, the Sudan, and Egypt, certain mutilations of the external genitalia of the female are practiced. One of these mutilations, infibulation, and its successional operation, defibulation, is—detail for detail—to be found in but one other region of the world, namely, among a few isolated Indian tribes of Peru, and possibly Central and South America.

Infibulation or "sewing up" of the vulva, and defibulation or "unsewing" of the vulva, are operations of so remarkable a nature as to render their peculiar geographic distribution, North Africa and certain regions of the New World, of more than ordinary interest. Are we here concerned with a case of independent invention, or is some other explanation, such as diffusion, more probable? But let us proceed to several early accounts of these operations as performed in North Africa and then follow it with descriptions which have been given of the operations as practiced in the New World.

Peney, surgeon-in-chief to the French Forces in the Sudan, writing in 1859 of the practices then current among the Sudanese tribes which had come under his observation, gives the following account of infibulation:

Between the age of seven and eight years the girl is handed over to the matron whose office it is to perform the operation. Some days beforehand the mother of the family invites all her female relations and acquaintances to assemble in her abode, and the ceremony is preceded with food and merriment.

When the hour comes, the child is laid on a bed and held down and in position by the assembled women, while the matron, kneeling between the patient's thighs, begins by slicing off the tip of the clitoris and the edges of the inner lips. Then the razor shears along the rims of the outer lips, removing a ribbon of flesh about 2 cm. wide. It lasts between four and five minutes. In order to drown the shrieks of the girl, the assembled guests and kin raise the loudest and shrillest din conceivable until the process is over. Then, when the flowing blood has been staunched, the girl is laid flat on her back, her legs extended and tied firmly together so that she cannot walk, otherwise the desired effect would not be produced. Before leaving the girl to the healing process of nature, the matron introduces a hollow cylinder of wood, about as thick as a goose's feather, into the lower portion of the vagina, between the bleeding edges of the wound, and this is kept in place until the scar is completely formed. For purposes of micturition and menstruation this tiny orifice is all that remains of the vaginal outlet.[1]

Numerous similar accounts of the operation have been given by other observers since Peney's day,[2] one of the most recent being that given by the Seligmans for the Kababish, an Arab tribe of the Anglo-Egyptian Sudan.[3]

Peney describes defibulation as follows:

When the Nubian maiden marries, she has recourse to the wise woman, in order to have her vulva prepared and enlarged,

---

1 Dr. Peney, "Etudes sur ... Soudan," *Bull. de la Soc. de Geographie*, 4 ser. (Paris, 1859), T. 17, p. 339. Quoted in H. H. Ploss, M. Bartels, and P. Bartels, *Woman*, ed. by Eric Dingwall (London, 1935), Vol. 1, p. 357.

2 See Ploss *et al., op. cit.*, pp. 353–59.

3 C. G. and B. Z. Seligman, *The Kababish, A Sudan Arab Tribe* (Harvard African Studies; Cambridge, 1918), Vol. 3, pp. 105–86.

for the infibulated aperture is far too small and too inelastic—
because of the scars of connective tissue which surround it on
every side—to admit even the roughest and most merciless husband. So the expert matron intervenes and makes a longitudinal
slash, and intercourse takes place; but first the matron introduces a fresh tube or cylinder of wood or vegetable fibre and far
bulkier than the first, into the vagina, to the distance of 3 or 4
inches. This remains *in situ* for a fortnight until the new wound
has healed and scarred when its presence becomes unnecessary.[4]

Werne, writing at an earlier date than Peney, gives a very
similar description of infibulation as practiced among the tribes
immediately south of the first cataract of the Nile, but extends
the account of defibulation in several important details which
have since been fully corroborated by other observers.[5] Werne
writes:

When the girl whose virginity has been preserved in such a
revolting manner becomes a bride, further indecent cruelties are
practised. One of the women who perform infibulation visits the
bridegroom immediately before the marriage in order to obtain
exact measurements of his member. She then makes to measurement, a sort of phallus of clay or wood and by its aid she incises
the scar for a certain distance and leaves the instrument wrapped
round with a rag—in the wound in order to keep the edges from
adhering again. Then the wedding feast is celebrated with
hideous din, the man leads his bride home—every step she takes
means pain—and without giving the fresh wounds time to heal
or scar, he exercises his marital privileges.

Before a child can be born, the vulva has to be opened again
throughout its length, but, after delivery, infibulation is again
inflicted, according to the husband's orders, either to the original
or other dimensions: and so the process continues.[6]

[4] Peney, *loc. cit.*
[5] See Ploss *et al., op. cit.,* pp. 359–63.
[6] F. Werne, *Reise durch Sennar nach Mandera, Nasub, Cheli im Lande
zwischen dem blauen Nil und dem Atbara* (Berlin, 1852), p. 25.

With these accounts may be compared that given by Reich of the ceremony customary among the Conibos of the Rio Ucayali in Peru. Reich writes:

> As soon as a girl attained to mature age, a great feast was made in which a fermented drink made of manioc roots, called *maschato*, played an important part. After the girl had been made so intoxicated by this beer that she was quite unconscious, the operation began. She was stretched out on three poles of *palo de balsa*, and in the presence of the whole noisy assembly an old experienced woman cut round the *introitus vaginae* with a knife of bamboo and severed the hymen from the *labia pudendi* so that the clitoris was set quite free. The old sorcerers rubbed some medical herbs into the bleeding parts, and after a while introduced an artificial penis, made of clay, into the vagina of the maiden, the thing being exactly the same size as the penis of the man betrothed to her. Thereafter she was considered properly prepared to marry, and was given over to her future husband.[7]

From this account, though it is far from detailed, it will be perceived that infibulation is probably secured as a result of the incision made around the *introitus vaginae*. If this were not so, there would hardly be any point to the insertion of the artificial penis into the vagina. Evidently this part of the ceremony is designed to secure an opening in the vagina corresponding to the diameter of the penis of the betrothed.

The only respects in which the operation appears to differ from that customary in North Africa is that in the New World the excisions of the labia are not as extensive as those practiced in the Old World, nor is the clitoris removed as it is in most parts of North Africa. The Indians would seem to have more consideration for the girl than do the Africans, for, unlike the

[7] A. Reich and F. Stagellmann, "Bei den Indianern der Urubamba und des Envira," *Globus*, Bd. 83 (1903), p. 134. Quoted in R. Karsten, *The Civilization of the South American Indians* (London, and New York, 1926), p. 177.

latter, they first render her pleasantly unconscious before commencing the operation. Another difference is that while in the Old World infibulation is generally performed at between six and eight years of age and defibulation is performed some years later, immediately before marriage, in the New World both operations are, as it were, telescoped into one, being performed at the same time "at a mature" age, sometime before marriage.

It may be that it is not correct to speak of defibulation among the Conibos; the purpose of the "infibulatory" incision and the introduction of the model of the betrothed's penis into the vagina seems to be exactly the same as that of the North Africans, namely, postmarital chastity, "the locking of the gate," as one Egyptian woman put it, to all but the husband. In North Africa, however, the value put upon premarital chastity is so high that infibulation is performed as soon as the girl begins to leave the period of early childhood behind her. In the New World areas under discussion, premarital chastity is not particularly valued, whereas postmarital chastity is; hence it may readily be inferred why in these areas infibulation and defibulation are delayed until the girl is ready for marriage and are performed together.

If infibulation actually occurs among the Conibos, it is obvious that a true defibulation must be performed before childbirth can occur. Information on this point is not available. If a true infibulation is not produced, the ceremonies and the operations among the Conibos, at the very least, sufficiently resemble those which have been described for North Africa to constitute a striking parallel. Is this parallel due to independent invention or diffusion? It is, of course, impossible to say with any degree of certainty, but from the differences which characterize the practices it would seem more probable that independent invention or development is the correct explanation.

Since we know that circumcision, incision, excision, and various other mutilations of the external genitalia are practiced among many South American tribes [8]—in itself a fact of considerable interest—it is very likely that mutilations resembling infibulation and defibulation are more widely practiced in South America than has thus far been reported.

[8] E. Grandidier, *Voyage dans l'Amérique du Sud, Perou et Bolivie* (Paris, 1861), p. 129. R. Andree, *Ethnographische Parallelen und Vergleiche* (Leipzig, 1899), pp. 201–4. Karsten, *op. cit.*, pp. 176–78. J. B. von Spix and C. F. Ph. von Martius, *Reise in Brasilien;* 3 Bde. (Munich, 1823–31). Fernandez de Souza, in *Revista trimensal do instituto historico e geographico do Brasil,* Ser. 3 (1848), p. 497. J. Gumilla, *Historia natural, civil y geográfica de las naciones del Rio Orinoco* (Barcelona, 1791), Vol. 1, pp. 118 seq.

26. Circumcision

The operation of cutting away the whole or part of the foreskin of the penis is a custom of wide ethnic distribution. Its worldwide practice, together with the widely preferred use of a stone knife in performance, would suggest a great antiquity for the operation. The origin of the practice is unknown. Alone among the peoples of the earth the Indo-Germanic, the Mongol, and the Finno-Ugrian-speaking peoples were unacquainted with the practice. Wherever the operation is performed as a traditional rite, it is done either before or at puberty, and sometimes, as among some Arabian peoples, immediately before marriage.

Among the ancient Egyptians, boys were generally circumcised between the ages of six and twelve years. Among the Ethiopians, the Jews, the Muslims, and a few other peoples, the operation is performed shortly after birth. Among most other peoples who practice it, the operation is performed at puberty. At both age periods the operation is regarded as of the profoundest religious significance. For the Jews it represents the fulfillment of the covenant between God and Abraham (Gen. 17:10–14), the first divine command of the Pentateuch, that every male child shall be circumcised. That Christians are not obliged to be circumcised is first recorded in Acts 15. The operation at puberty represents a beginning of the initiation into manhood and the leaving behind of childhood.

At whatever age performed, circumcision usually signifies the formal admission of the individual into his group or to the achievement of a certain status, thus fixing his social position, rights, and duties. To this day the operation among many peoples remains a necessary preliminary to the admission of proselytes. It is said that Pythagoras (c. 530 B.C.) had to submit to the operation before he was permitted to study in Egyptian temples. One of the best-known, but not the earliest, representations of circumcision, occurring on the wall of an Egyptian tomb at Saqqara dating to about 2400 B.C., presents scenes showing a boy whose wrists are being held by a man who stands behind him, while the priest stoops to perform the operation. Earlier representations and descriptions indicate that the practice was already well established in Egypt as early as 4000 B.C. and probably earlier. In Egypt it apparently was at first principally performed on the priestly class, being later adopted by the warrior classes, the nobility, and royalty.

There are numerous theories concerning the origin of circumcision. The following constitute a representative sample: it represents a blood offering to the gods, in order to maintain the latter's immortality and also to extend the life of the individual; it is a substitute for sacrifice; it is a dedication; the sacrifice of a part to ensure the welfare of the whole; the cutting off and preservation of part of oneself ensures preservation after death, and reincarnation; it represents the atonement made for incestuous desires entertained in childhood, unconsciously expiated by the fathers through their sons; since the foreskin often exerts a constricting effect it was considered magically to inhibit fertility, hence the necessity of its removal; finally, it has been suggested that it was practiced for purely hygienic reasons.

There is probably some truth in some of these conjectures, perhaps in all, but precisely how much or how little it is impossible to say. The origins of the practice are as dark as an Egyptian night. A lucky series of archaeological finds may some day provide a more exact understanding of the origin of the custom.

Female circumcision or excision is widely practiced in such places as New Guinea, Australia, the Malay archipelago, Ethiopia, Africa, Egypt, southern Europe, South America and by various Islamic peoples of western Asia and India. The operation consists in cutting away the whole or part of the external genitalia. Strabo, the Greek geographer, in the first century A.D. noted female circumcision among the Egyptians. In Egypt the operation appears to have been performed upon females at puberty at least several centuries before Strabo reported it. It is quite possible that female circumcision antedates male circumcision.

From the medical aspect the operation consists in removal of the foreskin to allow its free retraction beyond the glans penis. The foreskin or prepuce consists of a double layer of skin which more or less completely covers the glans penis. Under the inner layer of foreskin are situated a number of glands which secrete a cheeselike substance called smegma. Accumulation of smegma beneath the foreskin may result in great discomfort and may serve as the source of a rather penetrating odor. The balanitis, or inflammation, of the glans penis, which to some extent may be observed in the uncircumcised, is eliminated by circumcision. So, too, is the often associated phimosis or narrowing of the external orifice of the penis relieved. It is noteworthy that in India the Hindus, who do not circumcise ritually, suffer far more frequently from cancer of the penis than the Muslims, who practice ritual circumcision usually at the age of ten to twelve years. Among the Jews, who perform the operation shortly after birth, cancer of the penis virtually never occurs.

In the Western world the operation has been widely practiced in some countries as a hygienic procedure. In many hospitals it is routinely performed upon the newborn unless there is some objection. It has been felt by some authorities that circumcision of the newborn may be psychologically traumatic and that it should be performed later only if symptoms are serious enough to warrant surgical intervention. It is, however, a question whether the operation would be less traumatic to the older child.

27. *Marriage Rites: Rites of Courtship and Marriage*

Marriage is a social institution, recognized by custom or law, in which one or more men or one or more women enter into a union with one another with the assumption of permanency. Since marriage constitutes the basis of the family, and in that connection alone entails obligations, responsibilities, duties, and rights of many kinds, it is everywhere considered a basic social institution, although the degree to which it is so considered, curiously enough, varies in different societies.

In our own societies of the Western world we often hear it said, especially by young people, that marriage concerns the principals only, those who intend to become husband and wife, and should not be "interfered with" by others. This is a particularly young view of the meaning of marriage, and it is as wrongheaded and unsound as it could possibly be. The fact is, of course, that the contemplated marriage of a male and female, even in the societies of the Western world, involves a whole network of human relationships. In the marriage of a male and a female there are at once brought into close relationships fathers and mothers, brothers and sisters, and other relations, and new relationships are in this way created, entailing very clearly defined new forms of behavior. Furthermore, marriage is an economic institution, usually affecting the economic rights of others, not merely of husband and wife but of their parents and often of uncles and aunts, brothers and sisters, and the community.

Clearly, then, every contemplated marriage produces a certain amount of social disequilibration and tension. Marriage is virtually everywhere regarded as a most serious event and is therefore safeguarded and approached in a manner designed to achieve a return to equilibrium and to reduce the tensions resulting from such a critical change, in the lives of so many, to a normal level. Toward this end most societies have developed practices preliminary to marriage which are calculated to enable those contemplating forming a permanent union to make sure that they really want to enter into such a union. In many societies these arrangements are formalized at an early age. For example, among the Muria of Bastar State in India, the village dormitory, or *ghotul,* a typical institution to be found in many other parts of India, as well as in many other parts of the rest of the world, provides such opportunities for boys and girls. There is no fixed age at which boys and girls may claim admission to the dormitory, although very little boys and girls are not permitted to sleep in it. In the dormitory boys and girls pair off together. In the older type of dormitory such pairings were more or less permanent and led eventually to marriage. In the more modern form of dormitory exclusive associations are forbidden and partners are constantly changed. In this way the prospective bride and bridegroom may discover each other and so ensure a stable union in marriage. Verrier Elwin's account of this institution, *The Muria And Their Ghotul,*[1] is the best account of these youthful dormitories, as well as one of the best ethnographies, we have.

It should be clear, however, that the premarital sexual freedom which is the rule in nonliterate societies is an efficient means of allowing young people to get to know each other

[1] New York: Oxford University Press, 1947.

intimately before they select, or have selected for them, a mate. In some societies prospective husband and wife meet for the first time at their own wedding, as was frequently the case in China, Japan, and many parts of India. Such customs, however, did not preclude the ceremonial practice of betrothal rites even in those cases, as among the Australian aborigines, in which an old man was betrothed to a girl yet unborn. For example, among most Australian aboriginal peoples everyone born is born in the relationship, as the Dieri put it, of *noa-mara* to someone else, that is, in the relation of "spouseship." Thus, only members of certain totems belonging to certain moieties of a clan are in the relation of marriageability to one another. Among the Arunta of central Australia a man may promise his friend of the correct totemic moiety that his next daughter shall be his wife. Among the Dieri of southeast Australia, betrothal of children may be arranged by their respective mothers, with the consent of the brothers of the mother of the girl. The fathers involved have no say in the matter. In every case there must be an exchange of a sister, own or tribal, of the boy, who is thereby promised as a wife to the brother, own or tribal, of the girl. The new relation between them is called *tippa-malku,* and as an evidence that the promise has been made, the navel strings of the two children are tied with emu feathers and different-colored strings, a charming custom.

Courtship customs vary among the peoples of the world most remarkably. Among the Dayaks of Borneo a young man will wake a girl and offer her a present of some betel nuts carefully wrapped in siris leaf. If she accepts, this is interpreted as an encouragement and signifies that the young man may stay and talk with her. Before departing, he will sometimes leave under her pillow a necklace formed of seed of the balong fruit, a powerful-smelling pungent.

In a Kayan or Kenyah house in Borneo, cigarettes made from tobacco wrapped in banana leaves must be given, and a girl will give to her lover a cigarette tied in a very special way if she wishes him to stay longer. Among the Kayan, if all goes well and the visits of the youth are encouraged, it is the custom for the young man to rest his head in the lap of the girl, who proceeds, with a pair of brass tweezers, to remove his eyebrows and lashes! The girl will frequently play a sort of Jew's harp to attract the youth to her room, where he will spend the night. Following this stage the young man persuades someone to inform the girl's parents of his desire to marry her. The latter are, of course, completely surprised—at least they pretend to be —and if the suitor is accepted, he then presents a brass gong or a valuable bead to the girl's family as a pledge of his sincerity. The girl sends a necklace of beads to her future husband. When the courtship has reached this stage, public recognition must be secured. Some friend or relation informs the chief, who then decides whether the match is a suitable one or not. If he considers the union undesirable it never takes place. If he approves the match, the betrothal is formally announced and the omens are then consulted. If the cries of certain birds and deer are heard near the house, it is considered a bad omen, and a wise and knowledgeable person will be sent into the forest to seek out good omens and those sufficiently favorable to counterbalance any bad ones. The whistle of the trogon, the chirp of the spider hunter, and a hawk's flight high in the heavens from right to left are considered good omens. Should the omens be persistently bad, the marriage will be postponed for a year, and then the omens will be consulted again. The young man will meanwhile have left the village, and before his departure he will have made sure of having another girl in prospect should the omens in the village once more prove unfavorable. Should they prove favorable, the marriage will take place early, usually after the harvest, when there is a new moon, which is considered the luckiest time.

On the day before the marriage the bridegroom makes sure of collecting a good store of betel nuts so the guests will have something to chew during the wedding ceremony. The Kayan bridegroom or his people make the girl's parents many presents, the quantity varying with the social position of the parties. Such presents are called the bride wealth, and are almost always made to the bride's parents, in compensation, among other things, for the economic loss of the daughter. In other societies of the more civilized kind it is the bride's family that supplies the bride wealth, which goes wholly or in part to the bridegroom as a dowry.

But to return to our Kayans, when the wedding occurs in the bride's house, friends of each party are invited to the wedding and congregate in the long gallery of the house. Early in the morning, the bridegroom, with his best man and a number of warriors in full war dress, arrive by boat at the bride's house. They must arrive by boat, because this is the custom, even though the bridegroom's house is next door to the bride's. They carry with them, in many cases, large brass gongs, which are set down close to one another in the long gallery. Upon these the bride will step from one to the other. Presents are brought and heaped up outside her door. Then the bridegroom and his party attempt to force open her door but are repelled by the bride's party, and a sham fight ensues. This is repeated several times, until the bridegroom and his group succeed in entering the bride's room, only, too often, to find that the bride has escaped into one of her neighbor's rooms. The bride is lost and cannot be found. Whereupon the bridegroom seats himself in the center of the room and smokes cigarettes. The bride, taking pity on his lot, will then appear with her girlfriends, but the bridegroom deigns to take no notice of her. It is at this time that the dowry is arranged, and more gongs are added to those already offered in payment. A pig is killed, and if the entrails show favorable signs the blood is sprinkled over everyone present by a *dayong*, a woman possessing certain holy skills. With this the *dayong* blesses the young couple and wishes them great happiness and many children. Bride and bridegroom then step from gong to gong seven times, after which the ceremony is ended, except for a feast held in the evening.

It will be noted from this account of Kayan courtship, betrothal, and marriage how at every step the seriousness and the responsibilities arising out of the contemplated relationship are infused with value and importance by the rites and ceremonial forms of behavior associated with them. It should also be noted that betrothal and marriage ceremonials constitute rites of passage in which the phases of separation, transition, and incorporation are clearly seen. Separation from her own sexual group and from her parents' house is acted out in the assault by the bridegroom's party upon the bride's room and party. Her party doesn't want to let her go, but finally the bridegroom's party succeeds in entering the room only to find the bride fled back to a neighbor's room. She then voluntarily appears before the bridegroom with her girlfriends, thus signaling her transition from her former sex group into her new intended status. But the bridegroom cannot accept her until she has been paid for. When this transaction is completed, she and the bridegroom will together complete the transition by walking over the gongs seven times, thus migrating from their former status of the unmarried to the married state and incorporation into its rights and responsibilities as adults. The most significant formal communal rite of incorporation which terminates the proceedings is the feast held in celebration of the marriage. This is the ceremony of communal incorporation. Acts of incorporation with individual meaning which serve to unite the two young people involved begin in the courting period. In our example of the Dayaks and Kayans this is seen in the giving and exchange of gifts, the betel nut, the balong fruit, the necklace, and the plucking of eyebrows and eyelashes. All these are essentially rites of union, of incorporation, as is also the sojourn of the youth with the girl during the night.

That various groups as well as the marrying principals are involved in marriage is recognized by and in the collective rites

of incorporation. The collective significance of marriage cele-
brates either the joining of one or the other of the marrying
partners to new groups or the uniting of the two groups by the
marriage. Such collective incorporation rites take the form of
exchange of gifts, exchange of sisters, ritual dances, betrothal
and wedding feasts, exchange of visits, rounds of visits, putting
on the dress of married men and women, and the like.

In one form or another such rites of courtship, betrothal, and
marriage occur in every human society, and they serve to underscore once again the fact that in such societies the union of a
male and female in marriage is regarded as a most critical event,
because it is fully understood how serious such a relationship is
for the functioning and stability of the society as a whole, since
marriage is regarded as not merely affecting the marrying partners alone but the society in its entirety. And this is what the
rites of courtship, betrothal, and marriage are designed to im-
press upon everyone.

Betrothal as an institution is variously conceived in different
societies. For example, in some societies this transition period
is regarded as an opportunity for emphasizing once more the
separation of the two young people from their former sex
group, and neither may indulge in sex relations with each other
or anyone else. A child born to the girl during this period
would not find a proper place in its society. In other societies
the young pair have sexual relations during the period of betrothal, and a child born to the girl during this period is accepted into the society without the least strain.

Among the Mende of Sierra Leone a young man interested
in marriage does not approach the girl himself but sends as his
deputies a small party of friends, among whom must be a
woman. If he is an older man already married, he may send
with this party one of his wives, who will be able to speak with
the best of authority on the virtues of the would-be suitor as
a husband. When the party arrives at the girl's home, appropriate presents will be offered, indicating the seriousness of the

errand upon which the visitors are engaged. An interview with the parents having been granted, there will also be a present for the girl, accompanied by some such pretty remarks as: "We see a beautiful gem in your house, and we come to get it; we bring this present for her."

In spite of the fact that a girl may be betrothed almost as soon as she is born, if she is old enough to make a choice—the present having been shown her and the object of the deputation explained to her—and she accepts the present, even though she may never have seen the aspirant to her hand, her acceptance of the gift is tantamount to consenting to the betrothal, and she will send her suitor a return gift, thus announcing to him the accomplishment of his desire. The way is then clear to treating with the parents, an expensive affair involving "wine money" in the form of rum and gin, and the greater the quantity of "wine money" the greater the hold upon the girl, who then has little chance of breaking her engagement.

Among the American Indians, courtship and betrothal customs, as well as marriage customs, differed considerably, but in general there was little chance for courtship, and both betrothal and marriage were not a matter of elaborate ceremony. Girls were strictly guarded. As a Chiricahua Apache informant put it, "The girl was carefully watched by her folks. Because of this it was necessary to have someone approach the parents and speak for you if you wanted to marry a girl. It was almost impossible to court a girl. Men had to do it on the sly." [2] Premarital control brought the suitors or their representatives directly to the parents, which allowed the latter to choose their sons-in-law and fix the terms of marriage. There were, however, ways for young people who were attracted to each other to meet, as for example, at a chaperoned dance or at the store, but almost always in the presence of others and frequently without speaking.

[2] M. E. Opler, *An Apache Life-Way* (Chicago: University of Chicago Press, 1941), p. 143.

It is interesting that where there is so little chance for court-ship, as among the Chiricahua Apache, love ceremonies, de-signed to engender love, should flourish. Some women and men have the power to bring this about and, upon payment, will perform the necessary ceremonies, mainly involving the playing of the four-holed flageolet, made of carrizo. The danger in these love ceremonies is that the individual toward whom they are directed may learn of them and then use counterpower to resist them. A butterfly, the sun, and water are also used in the love ceremonies. Appealing to the sun and water, the girl's love (or the man's) is made to fly toward the supplicant as on the wings of a butterfly. The word for love is in fact related to the word for water. The desired one, lured by flageolet music, is to be-come aimless and as irresponsible as the butterfly and is to be enmeshed in a net of "ropes" of the sun (sunbeams, sometimes symbolized by pieces of cord). There must be contact with the person to be influenced. Water may be playfully splashed on him. Mimicking the sun motif, a beam of light may be directed toward him from some shiny object; a sticky leaf may be flicked at him; a butterfly or a caterpillar may be dropped in his bed. In lieu of the person, a piece of his clothing or a strand of his hair will do.

It is a likely speculation that such practices are common, and they are, indeed, widespread among the peoples of the world where opportunities for courtship are at a minimum and oppor-tunities for the sexes to meet are minimal. It is of some interest to note that women, especially, in highly civilized regions of the world, who for one reason or another have failed to circulate much, have been known to employ experts in the necessary arts designed to cause some hapless male to yield to their need for love.

In some societies courtship of the girl is not by her would-be suitor but by the parents. Among the Senufo of Africa, the youth desirous of marrying a girl is careful not to let his inten-tion be known to her or her family. But he watches the comings and goings of her parents, and when he sees the girl's mother go to the bush to bring back wood, he awaits her return on the road and rushes to relieve her of her load, which he then carries for her on his head. Later, he helps the girl's father carry pieces of termite nest for the hens. A few days later the young man himself gathers wood and carries it to the home of the girl. He then follows this with gifts of kola nuts, a chicken, and finally some cowries, which he presents to the girl's father. The latter then invites his family and a village elder to a confabulation, at which he explains that a certain young man has been most obliging and helpful to him and it would make him happy to reward this youth by giving him his daughter in marriage. If the assembly approves, the elder informs the suitor of the success of his suit. But all is not yet achieved, for when the cultivating season approaches, the young man must collect his brothers and friends, and they must all heave to and plow his future father-in-law's field. When the field has been sown, the suitor must come to weed. He buys the girl's entire family millet beer, and with that the official betrothal begins.

The girl may be far from marriageable age. Until she is nubile she remains at her father's house. During the intervening period the groom must assist her family with his labor and resources. When the girl reaches nubility she is given to the groom on payment of a gift of five to ten cowrie francs to the father and a gift of the same value to the mother. When the young couple have lived together for a month, the girl's father fetches her home for a stay in his house for some three months, after which she is returned to her husband upon payment of ten cowrie francs. Again she may stay only a month with her husband, when she is again claimed by her father for another three months, after which, upon payment of another ten francs, she is permanently returned to her husband.

Whatever the forms of courtship, betrothal, and marriage we find among the peoples of the world, their ceremonial functions are clearly designed to make the passage from one status, by separation, transition, and incorporation into the others, as smooth and as significant as possible. Every marriage involves a disturbance of social equilibrium, modifying the relationships of everyone concerned. There is also a highly significant economic aspect to the marriage relationship, and this is especially emphasized during the betrothal period, when the young man must through gifts, labor, and his other resources balance accounts by indemnifying those suffering the loss for the deprivation of their group of the value of the female. In many societies, it should be noted, the young man goes to live temporarily either in the village or in the home of his in-laws, and there works for them and his own wife and children.

With ceremony and ritual, society is enabled to achieve the smooth working of many of its parts by putting a gloss, with the appropriate celebrations, over changes that might sometimes be difficult to accept, and to give proper value to those separations, transitions, and incorporations through which most human beings will pass.

In our own society, coming-out parties, debutante balls, and the like are anthropologically similarly interesting examples falling into the class of courtship and marriage rituals, and also of the rites of passage, and economically, of the marketing mentality, not to mention the principle of conspicuous consumption.

28. *Birth Rites*

In his exquisite book about childhood, *Early One Morning,* Walter de la Mare writes: "There are few things in the world so sure of a welcome in any human mind as a creature brand-new to this life of ours, young in time, and of a brief earthly experience." And, as De la Mare goes on to add, "Its kind matters little: beast, bird, or fish ... the human impulse is the same. A peculiar wistfulness is mingled with our pleasure in them. We realize their comparative helplessness, yet marvel at their finish, competence and vigour." And this is how it has always been, and especially for the young of human kind. For his own continued existence, man has always been dependent on his successful reproduction, and not one whit less upon the successful reproduction of plants and animals. Man has always known that his own continued existence was dependent on the continued existence of other plants and animals, but he has also always understood that his continued existence was just as much dependent upon the sun and the clouds in the sky, and therefore he has considered himself interdependent and interrelated with the whole of nature, and held it sacred. The sacred, like the profane, is an attitude of mind. The sacred is a veneration, a reverence, for those things regarded as holy, that is, partaking of the supernatural. And nothing can be more sacred than life, especially human life.

For the two million or so years of man's existence on this

earth, up to very recent days, human life was a precarious thing. The way of life was food-gathering and hunting, and the size of a population under such conditions could be no other than small, very much like that of the Bushmen of the Kalahari desert of today. Forty to fifty people has been about the average size of such communities. The average expectation of life was a little more than thirty-three years, and infant mortality was high. Life was therefore a precious thing, for in addition to its individual tenuousness, the reduction of the group to virtual extinction must have occurred and been witnessed again and again. Furthermore, people living at a subsistence level are continually threatened with extinction unless they are constantly able to provide food for themselves and their dependents. To be near starvation is not a rare experience for food-gathering, hunting peoples to this day. Man has always been at the mercy of the elements, and his attempts to control and compel those elements to do his bidding are accompanied by rites and rituals designed to make proper acknowledgment of the response made to his supplications.

The long period of pregnancy and the pain and travail associated with childbirth further serves to emphasize the precariousness and preciousness of human life. Indeed, I have argued elsewhere that one of the functions served by childbirth pains, so-called labor pains, is to emphasize at this critical time how thin the thread is by which human life hangs and to focus attention on its sanctity. The practical effect of this is to enlist the support of everyone concerned to bring the pregnancy to a successful issue. This means not only the invocation, the appeal to the supernatural, but the actual practice of what is considered to be helpful in ensuring a successful completion of the pregnancy. Hence, everything necessary is done to protect the pregnant woman against whatever may be considered inimical to a satisfactory outcome. It is not only the child's preservation that is at stake, but also the mother's. A woman who loses a child may have another, but a woman who is lost in pregnancy, even though her child may be preserved, is lost to the replenishment of the group, and this may sometimes make all the difference between the survival and extinction of that group. As in non-literate societies today, a barren woman in prehistoric societies was almost certainly considered redundant, and it is a fact worth remarking that this view of the barren woman persists in the most civilized societies of our own time, even where the excess of fertile women runs into the millions. Rites to preserve and enhance fertility are universal, and perhaps in our own time "the population explosion" may be considered to be the ultimate tribute to the efficacy of those rites. However that may be, the pregnant woman has in all societies been regarded with special care and reverence. Every society prescribes what she may and may not do during her pregnancy, and how others must behave toward her. Volumes could be filled with a description of these practices, and it would be pointless to refer to even a few of them here, except in general terms, for the purpose of all these practices, whatever form they take, is to bring the mother and baby safely through the pregnancy. At the same time numerous social functions are accomplished by these practices which serve, among other things, to return everyone involved to a state of equilibrium.

Pregnancy is one of the crises of life, and if a pregnant woman is in a special state during that period, so is her husband, and both of them may not resume their former way of life until they have successfully passed through this critical period. There are ceremonies through which they must pass before they can be restored to customary secular life. In the case of the husband there is the well-known custom of couvade, in which the father goes into a sort of confinement designed to imitate the processes of pregnancy, childbirth, and postparturitive recovery. Judging from the anxieties modern fathers frequently experience with the childbirths undergone by their wives, this is from many points of view not such a bad idea. In fact, there are a number of cases on record in our own society of men who have so identified themselves with their wives' conditions that they have themselves had to go to hospital with a bad case of piles! Hemorrhoids are a poor substitute for a baby, and one of the functions, no doubt, served by the couvade is to help allay and reduce the anxieties of the father, while at the same time underscoring the responsibilities of his paternity. The rites associated with the couvade are clearly designed to emphasize the passage of the father from one status to another, that is, from a mere husband to a husband who is also a father, one who has assumed new obligations to his family and to society. Such rites are called rites of passage, after a famous account of them first given in 1909 in a monograph entitled *Les Rites de Passage,* written by Arnold van Gennep and now obtainable in an English translation, *The Rites of Passage.*[1]

Rites of passage refer specifically to the ceremonies performed at those critical periods in the life of the individual, or life crises, such as birth, puberty, marriage, becoming a parent, becoming an adult, and death. Van Gennep recognized three principal phases in all rites of passage: separation (*séparation*), transition (*marge*), and incorporation (*agrégation*).

Rites of passage are performed in specific application not only to the individual but to critical periods in the development of the phenomena of the natural world, such as the seasons. Since the changing seasons vitally affect the lives of everyone, it is of the greatest importance to ensure the proper passage of the one into the other. When winter comes, it is true that spring cannot be far behind, and everyone knows that if the customary ceremonies were not performed, one season would still follow upon another. But what everyone also knows is that if the proper rites of passage are not carried out there is a real danger that plants and animals will not multiply, the rains will not come, and the rivers and waterholes will dry up. So it is a good thing to help winter on its way and enable it to become the

1 Chicago: University of Chicago Press, 1961.

spring it should turn into so that the summer becomes what it ought to be.

As Van Gennep recognized, always the principle that runs through the performance of rites of passage is that of renewal, of regeneration, the principle that characterizes the whole of life and the workings of the universe, however it is conceived, as well. An attempt has been made to refine Van Gennep's work and to refer to life crisis ceremonies involving the individual as rites of passage, whereas those affecting all or most of the members of the group are referred to as rites of intensification. But the fact is that almost certainly in all prehistoric societies and certainly in all nonliterate societies today the life crises of the individual affect all or most members of the group, whether they actively participate in the ceremonies or not by being physically present at them. However, it is useful to recognize that rites of passage performed specifically in relation to the individual and similar rites performed in relation to the group, whether in connection with seasonal changes or otherwise, are distinguishable to that extent, even though all remain rites of passage.

Here we are concerned with rites of passage celebrated by every society or culture of which we have knowledge at the birth of a child. It should be made clear from the outset that every rite, every custom, every practice within a society functions in relation to that society as a whole. Even though the members of the society may not be able to explain the history or even the meaning of the rite they are performing, it has both a history and a meaning, and we may be sure it plays an important role in the psychodynamics of the society.

Birth represents the separation from the mother of the infant who has spent all his time in her womb. He is now born into a family and into a society. The transition from birth to incorporation into the family and society as a member thereof is everywhere ceremonially recognized, with the group as a whole more or less intimately involved—with the exception, increasingly alas, of the highly sophisticated and overpopulated and agglutinated societies of the Western world.

I have already indicated something of the probable origin of rights of passage connected with birth, namely, the precariousness of the life of the newborn in particular and of all other human beings in general, and the virtually natural ceremonial recognition of these facts in the welcoming of the newborn and his incorporation into the group which he regenerates. When a child is born, a whole new web of relationships is generated. The birth of a child also means the birth of parents, grandparents, uncles, aunts, cousins, and siblings. Since kinship relations in nonliterate societies are extended to embrace every member of the group, with every birth a new reticulum of relationships is established in which every member of the group is involved. And not only is every member of the group involved in this network of relationships, but to a greater or lesser extent so is the whole of nature. In learning to be a member of his group the child gradually learns precisely what these relationships are, what his duties, rights, and obligations are in every specific connection. In such learning he is greatly assisted by the rites of passage from which he emerges, by graduated steps, better endowed to respond to the challenges of his environment. The first of these rites of passage are those associated with birth.

It is to be noted that the separation of the child from the mother presents certain basic physiological parallels upon which the social rites may be solidly based. For example, even though the placenta may be ejected and the third stage of labor thus completed, the infant is not considered separated from the mother until the umbilical cord has been cut. In many languages the placenta, very properly, bears reference to its maternal origin, as in the German *mutterkuchen,* or "mothercake." Among nonliterate peoples the placenta is generally regarded with special reverence and is accorded particular care. The placenta is the object of special rites and is generally afforded a proper habitation, for it is not infrequently considered to

contain an element with which the individual is at death reunited. The best-known example of this is from ancient Egypt,
where the placenta of the king was considered as the seat of the
immortal and heavenly soul, or Ka, which derived from the
moon. Among the Shilluk of the upper Nile the sacred kings
were buried where their placenta had been deposited when
they were born. The examples of this treatment of the placenta
from the many peoples of the world would fill volumes, but
what they all indicate is the transition from birth through death
as a single continuum. The placenta is not merely a thing, a
complex organ, as it is considered among us, but an intrinsic
part of the organism from which, though it is physically de-
tached, it is never spiritually removed, and with the spiritual
element which it contains the individual will ultimately be
reunited.

That the pain and travail of birth make a great impression
upon everyone is testified to by the fact that every society has
many references to this in its folklore, song, story, and secular
language; for example, among the Azande of Africa, a maternal
aunt will reproach a boy by reminding him of his mother's
pains during his birth. The duration of labor in the human
female for the firstborn is, on the average, fourteen hours, and
for subsequently born children an average of eight hours. This
is a long period of labor, and one of the functions such a lengthy
period of labor serves, I have already suggested, is to focus attention on the value and meaning of life and to produce in the
beholder a proper respect for it, whether he actually beholds
the process, which he more than likely does not, or merely
learns about it at second hand. In this the experience of the
sexes is asymetrical, since women alone are, almost everywhere,
permitted to assist with the delivery of the child. This fact
makes for certain clearly defined and distinctively different
roles played by the sexes at this time. The mother is too busy
having the baby to be herself engaged in any ceremonial procedures directly initiated by herself, although she is the object

of such ceremonies; on the other hand, her husband, the father
of her child, is generally engaged in ceremonies designed to
propitiate the spirits and to ensure a safe outcome of the parturition. Furthermore, it is at this time that he establishes
communication with ghosts and dead relatives, who are asked
to intercede with the appropriate spirits in behalf of mother
and child, as among the Azande. Thus, in such ceremonies the
past is brought into connection with the present and the future,
and this serves further to underscore the continuity of life and
of the group.

> Our birth is but a sleep and a forgetting:
>   The Soul that rises with us, our life's Star,
> Hath had elsewhere its setting,
>   And cometh from afar:
> Not in entire forgetfulness,
> And not in utter nakedness,
> But trailing clouds of glory do we come
>   From God, who is our home:
> Heaven lies about us in our infancy!

Wordsworth put it very beautifully in his "Ode: Intimations
of Immortality," this view of the new arrival into the community of man after a long and perilous journey "from afar,"
which so many people have held. "Trailing clouds of glory"—
to be celebrated and, in thanksgiving, to be commemorated. It
is, therefore, both with solemnity and in joy that birth rites are
everywhere ceremonially performed. Nothing in connection
with these ceremonies is ever perfunctorily done, and frequently
the ceremonies are extended over many days and continued at
intervals, so that the birth of every child becomes a memorable
occasion and not simply an incident in the flux of time, a statis-
tic, as among ourselves, to everyone but the immediate members
of the family.

It is of the greatest interest that so many of the rites associated
with birth should not only serve the useful social functions

they do but also that they should serve such valuable biological functions. For example, it is a widespread practice after the birth of the child to keep mother and child together in seclusion for a number of days. The reason given for this in many nonliterate societies is that the newborn is not yet properly a human being and requires some days to become one. There are all sorts of variations on this theme. Thus, an aborted baby among the Australian aborigines and other peoples is not regarded as human, and therefore no rites need be performed in connection with it. It may have been the wrong spirit baby from the wrong totemic moiety who entered the wrong woman and therefore chose this way out. It may therefore be buried or abandoned so that it will return to the spirit center from which it came and enter the appropriate woman at another time.

The biological benefits accruing to mother and infant when they are secluded are considerable. It is now well established that the excitement and fatigue of too many visitors are detrimental to the recuperation of both infant and mother from the parturitive process and to the normal psychophysiological developments which should follow that process. The protection afforded mother and infant by the seclusive practices followed by many peoples ensures, at least, that they will enjoy the opportunity of thriving in each other's presence in the continuing symbiotic relationship they have so long enjoyed, and not suffer from the fatigue and alarm resulting from exposure to milling crowds of visitors.

Bathing the child, washing his head, rubbing him with balm, during rites of purification and of separation from the mother, also have biologically beneficial effects. In nonliterate societies, where the child is often born into hygienically less than optimum conditions, the washing may indeed be physically as well as spiritually purifying, and the rubbing will certainly help to reassure and stimulate the sustaining systems.

We have in the past greatly underestimated the intelligence and powers of observation of nonliterate peoples. From our superior heights we were willing to give them very little credit for being both sensitive to the needs of human beings and understanding of many of the things we have only recently begun to learn. The customs and practices which we have looked upon as so quaint and barbaric have, as we have come to understand them, taken on far deeper meanings than they were first thought to have. A familiar rite associated with the welcoming of the newborn into the community, circumcision, has been practiced by many peoples. It is a typical separation rite, and whatever other ritual significances it may have, it is an operation of considerable hygienic value. It may never be known with certainty, but it is not unlikely that this operation originated in sound observation of the consequences of noncircumcision. Phimosis, infections, and other diseases are very much more frequent in the uncircumcised than in the circumcised. This observation may have constituted the original stimulus to perform the operation. That it would concomitantly be ritualized would follow from the fact that any part of the individual's body would, among other things, have to be protected on the principle of the part representing the whole.

While nonliterates enjoy a full secular life which is in no way ritualized, there are some things which obviously belong within the realm of the sacred and must be properly celebrated; hence, biologically recognized conditions, becoming the basis of social change, may frequently be ritualized because they fall within the realm of the sacred. For example, it is today the widely accepted belief among anthropologists that the incest prohibitions which are to be found in every human society are based on the recognition of the fact that marriage between close relatives is likely to multiply the chances of congenital abnormalities in the offspring of such unions. The social regulations which order marriage between persons in nonliterate societies are strictly adhered to and themselves become the object of distinctive ritual ceremonies.

It will be observed, then, that there is a continuous feedback between cultural and biological recognitions in human societies, each reciprocally affecting the other. Which came first, the biological or the ritual recognition? It is often difficult to decide. There can, however, be little doubt that in many cases the biological recognition came first, and that with man's habitual tendency to ritualize whatever touches upon the sacred and the highly valued, the ceremonial practices came second.

Without entering into any description of the rites of passage practiced by various peoples in connection with the birth of a child, or accounts of the hymns that may be sung, the incantations chanted, the talismans fastened on the child, the naming ceremonies, and the like, what, it may be asked, are the functions of these rites of passage?

In general the rites of passage connected with birth serve the function of reducing the tensions of everyone involved and of giving strong social emphasis to the fact that a new member of the community has arrived who has to be properly inducted into the society. Birth rites serve to draw the attention of every member of the group to the high value and sacredness of human life, the view, once more, that every living thing is holy and especially this frail creature that is man. Respect and reverence for life are in this way impressed upon everyone. Thankfulness and relief are expressed in an atmosphere which has compelled anxiety, and in which this precious freight, so uncertainly and painfully delivered, must have all the powers that can be invoked in his favor. Relatedness is born with the newborn: relatedness to himself by the members of his family and of his community. Relatedness implies obligations and responsibilities, and these are what birth rites are further designed to underscore. The acceptance of the new arrival is facilitated by these rites, new adjustments are made, and the unity and solidarity of the group are enhanced. Finally, the experience is once more afforded everyone of participating in the knowledge that man is a creature of the spirit, that he is still

> Nature's priest,
> And by the vision splendid
> Is on his way attended.

That man, indeed, is a transcendent spirit whose exterior semblance doth belie his soul's immensity. Yes, something more indeed than that concatenation of chemicals which some of our modern secular priests, the priests of science, have told us are over the counter worth no more than ninety-five cents. Others, and other peoples, have known better: a child is full of promises seeking to be realized, trailing clouds of glory, and his coming is a renewal of a life-giving promise which is at its least an assurance of the future and at its best the expectation that a welcome human being has joined the human procession who will be faithful to his trust and who will fulfill himself in service to his fellows and live his life with dignity and honor and with love.

It is something of all of this that, more or less clearly, all ceremonials connected with the birth of a child tend to make more emphatic by the values with which they endow the newly welcomed member of the society. And what we of the urbanized, civilized world have to learn is that we have not passed beyond the need of such ceremonial celebrations but that, on the contrary, we are more in need of them than ever. When, because of the irresponsible conduct of civilized men, overpopulation threatens to devalue the life of man, the true understanding of his value more than ever must be emphasized. Ceremonialism is not enough, but it is necessary, one of the necessary conditions which, together with the other necessary conditions, constitute the sufficient cause which makes the realization of humanity's promise possible.

Man is what he is because he is a symbol-using, symbol-making creature. It is by the imaginative use of his symbols that he deepens his understanding of the meaning of life and enriches it and gives dignity to the human condition. Of all the occasions most worth celebrating in life, the birth of a child is the most worthy. For here is a new beginning, the promise of fulfillment, a creature unique, the complete like of which there has never been before and will never be again, an innovation in the womb of time to be welcomed by his kindred spirits. What more worthy occasion for celebration, for ceremony, for ritual, and for song?

Index